Songs of Cheer

FOR CHILDREN

A Collection of Hymns and Songs suitable for use in the
Primary and Junior departments of our Sunday Schools.

Authorized by

MENNONITE GENERAL CONFERENCE

Compiled by

THE MUSIC COMMITTEE

Published by

MENNONITE PUBLISHING HOUSE

SCOTTDALE, PA.

1929

CONTENTS

A.133

All Glory, Laud and Honor

(ST. THEODULPH)

1

Theodulph, Bp. of Orleans. Tr. by J. M. Neale

Melchior Teschner, 1615
Music arranged

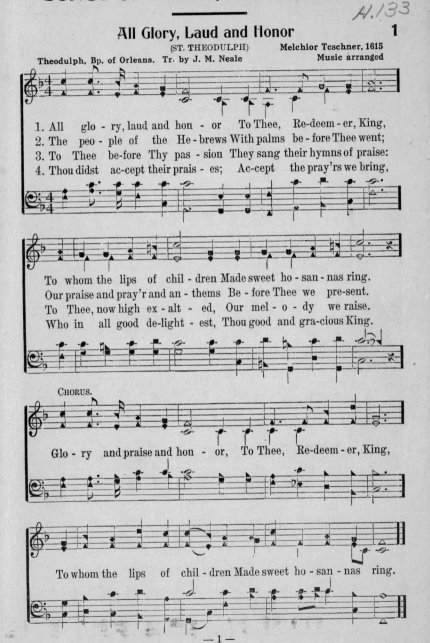

1. All glo - ry, laud and hon - or   To Thee,   Re-deem - er, King,
2. The peo - ple of   the He - brews With palms be - fore Thee went;
3. To Thee be-fore Thy pas - sion They sang their hymns of praise:
4. Thou didst ac-cept their prais - es;   Ac-cept   the pray'rs we bring,

To whom the lips of chil - dren Made sweet ho - san - nas ring.
Our praise and pray'r and an - thems Be - fore Thee we pre-sent.
To Thee, now high ex - alt - ed, Our mel - o - dy we raise.
Who in   all good de-light - est, Thou good and gra-cious King.

CHORUS.

Glo - ry and praise and hon - or,   To Thee,   Re-deem - er, King,

To whom the lips of chil - dren Made sweet ho - san - nas ring.

Happy Hearts

Lanta Wilson
Cheerfully.

C. A. Fyke

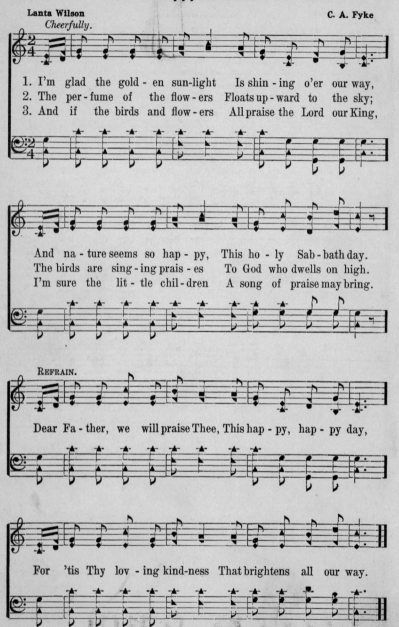

1. I'm glad the gold - en sun-light Is shin - ing o'er our way,
2. The per - fume of the flow - ers Floats up - ward to the sky;
3. And if the birds and flow - ers All praise the Lord our King,

And na - ture seems so hap - py, This ho - ly Sab - bath day.
The birds are sing - ing prais - es To God who dwells on high.
I'm sure the lit - tle chil - dren A song of praise may bring.

REFRAIN.

Dear Fa - ther, we will praise Thee, This hap - py, hap - py day,

For 'tis Thy lov - ing kind-ness That brightens all our way.

Praise Him! Praise Him!

Fanny J. Crosby

Chester G. Allen

1. Praise Him! praise Him! Je-sus, our blessed Re-deem-er! Sing, O earth—His
2. Praise Him! praise Him! Je-sus, our blessed Re-deem-er! For our sins He
3. Praise Him! praise Him! Je-sus, our blessed Re-deem-er! Heav'n-ly por-tals

won-der-ful love pro-claim! Hail Him! Hail Him! high-est arch-an-gels in
suf-fered and bled and died; He our Rock, our hope of e-ter-nal sal-
loud with ho-san-nas ring! Je-sus, Sav-iour, reigneth for-ev-er and

D. S.—*Praise Him! Praise Him! tell of His ex-cel-lent*

FINE.

glo-ry; Strength and hon-or give to His ho-ly name! Like a Shep-herd,
va-tion, Hail Him! hail Him! Je-sus, the Cru-ci-fied. Sound His prais-es!
ev-er: Crown Him! crown Him! Prophet and Priest and King! Christ is com-ing!

greatness, Praise Him! praise Him! ever in joy-ful song.

D. S.

Je-sus will guard His children, In His arms He carries them all day long;
Je-sus who bore our sor-rows, Love un-bound-ed, won-der-ful, deep and strong;
o-ver the world vic-to-rious, Pow'r and glo-ry un-to the Lord be-long;

Sing of the Mighty One

Frances R Havergal

W. A. Ogden

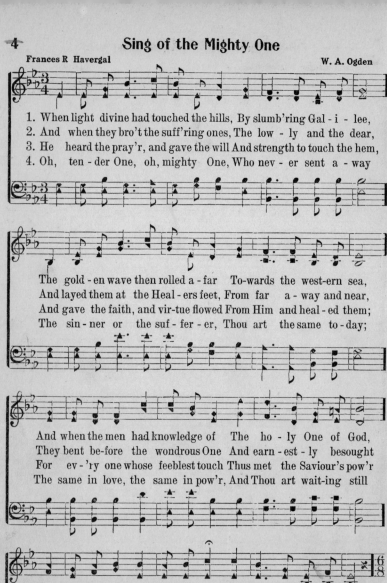

1. When light divine had touched the hills, By slumb'ring Gal - i - lee,
2. And when they bro't the suff'ring ones, The low - ly and the dear,
3. He heard the pray'r, and gave the will And strength to touch the hem,
4. Oh, ten - der One, oh, mighty One, Who nev - er sent a - way

The gold - en wave then rolled a - far To-wards the west-ern sea,
And layed them at the Heal - ers feet, From far a - way and near,
And gave the faith, and vir-tue flowed From Him and heal - ed them;
The sin - ner or the suf - fer - er, Thou art the same to - day;

And when the men had knowledge of The ho - ly One of God,
They bent be-fore the wondrous One And earn - est - ly besought
For ev - 'ry one whose feeblest touch Thus met the Saviour's pow'r
The same in love, the same in pow'r, And Thou art wait-ing still

They journeyed forth thro' all the land, And spread His fame a-broad.
That they might on - ly touch the hem A-round His garment wrought.
Rose up in perfect health and strength In that ac-cept-ed hour.
To heal the mul - ti - tude that come, Yea, who - so - ev - er will.

Sing of the Mighty One.—Concluded

Refrain. *Spirited.*

O sing of the lov - ing One! O sing of the heal - ing One!

O sing of the might-y One, He's just the same to - day!

Praise the Lord

5

C. E. P.

Charles Edw. Pollock

(For little children)

1. Lit - tle children, praise the Lord, Praise the Lord, praise the Lord,
2. Praise Him for His bless - ed Word, Bless - ed Word, bless - ed Word,
3. Praise Him for the Sab-bath day, Sab-bath day, Sab - bath day,
4. Praise Him for the Sun-day-school, Sun-day-school, Sun-day-school,
5. Praise Him for your teachers dear, Teachers dear, teach-ers dear,

Lit - tle chil - dren, praise the Lord, Praise ye the Lord.
Praise Him for His bless - ed Word, Praise ye the Lord.
Praise Him for the Sab-bath day, Praise ye the Lord.
Praise Him for the Sun-day-school, Praise ye the Lord.
Praise Him for your teach-ers dear, Praise ye the Lord.

6   Come, Thou Almighty King

Charles Wesley   ITALIAN HYMN   Felice Giardini, 1769

1. Come, Thou al-might-y King, Help us Thy name to sing, Help us to praise: Father! all-
2. Come, Thou incarnate Word, Gird on Thy mighty sword, Our pray'r attend: Come, and Thy
3. Come, Ho - ly Com-fort-er! Thy sacred wit - ness bear, In this glad hour; Thou who al-
4. To the great One in Three, The highest prais-es be, Hence evermore! His sov'reign

glo - ri-ous, O'er all vic - to - ri-ous, Come and reign o - ver us, Ancient of Days!
people bless, And give Thy Word success; Spir-it of ho - li-ness, On us de-scend!
mighty art, Now rule in ev-'ry heart, And ne'er from us depart, Spir-it of pow'r.
maj - es-ty May we in glo - ry see, And to e - ter - ni - ty Love and a - dore!

---

7   Jesus Shall Reign

H 56

Isaac Watts, 1719   DUKE STREET   John Hatton, c. 1793

1. Je - sus shall reign wher-e'er the sun Does His suc-ces-sive jour - neys run;
2. For Him shall end-less pray'r be made, And praises throng to crowd His head;
3. Blessings a-bound wher-e'er He reigns; The pris'nor leaps to lose His chains;
4. Let ev-'ry crea-ture rise and bring Pe - cu-liar hon-ors to our King,

His kingdom stretch from shore to shore, Till moons shall wax and wane no more.
His name, like sweet perfume, shall rise With ev'ry morn - ing sac - ri - fice.
The wea-ry find e - ter - nal rest, And all the sons of want are blest.
An - gels de-scend with songs a - gain, And earth repeat the loud A - men.

We Thank the Lord

Alma Bronce

D. F. Hodges

1. We thank the Lord for   dai-ly bread, Thank Him for home and friends;
2. We thank Him for this world so fair, And for the sun-ny hours;
3. Oh, then, re-joice and praise the Lord, For He loves us al - way;

We thank Him too for health and strength, For ev'ry gift He sends.
For bright blue skies and balm-y air, The trees, and birds, and flow'rs.
And thank Him now with grateful hearts, On this Thanksgiving day.

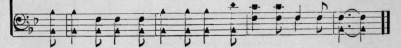

A Child's "Thank You"

Anon.   ST. BEES   John B. Dykes, 1862

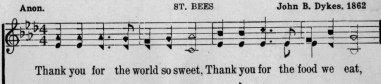

Thank you for   the world so sweet, Thank you for the food we   eat,

Thank you for the birds that sing, Thank you, God, for ev - 'ry-thing.

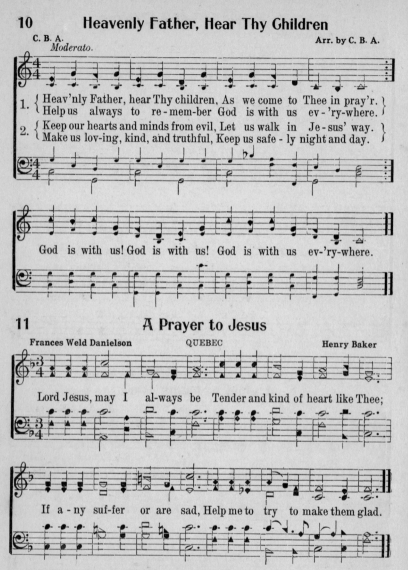

10   Heavenly Father, Hear Thy Children

C. B. A.

Moderato.

Arr. by C. B. A.

1. { Heav'nly Father, hear Thy children, As we come to Thee in pray'r.
   { Help us always to re-mem-ber God is with us ev-'ry-where.

2. { Keep our hearts and minds from evil, Let us walk in Je-sus' way.
   { Make us lov-ing, kind, and truthful, Keep us safe - ly night and day.

God is with us! God is with us! God is with us ev-'ry-where.

11   A Prayer to Jesus

Frances Weld Danielson   QUEBEC   Henry Baker

Lord Jesus, may I al-ways be Tender and kind of heart like Thee;

If a-ny suf-fer or are sad, Help me to try to make them glad.

(Recite the following verse with motions to get into reverent mood for a prayer or prayer-hymn.)

"We *fold our hands* that we may be
From earthly play and work set free;
We *bow our heads* as we draw near
The King of kings, our Father dear;
We *close our eyes*, that we may see
Nothing to take our thoughts from Thee."

Jesus, Friend of Little Children

12

Walter J. Mathams, 1882   J. H. Maunder

1. Je - sus, Friend of lit - tle chil - dren, Be a Friend to me,
2. Show me what my love should cher-ish, What, too, it should shun;
3. Step by step, O lead me on - ward, Up - ward in - to youth:
4. Nev - er leave me, nor for-sake me, Ev - er be my Friend,

Take my hand and ev - er keep me Close to Thee.
Lest my feet for poi - son flow - ers Swift should run.
Wis - er, stronger still, be - com - ing, In Thy truth.
For I need Thee from life's dawn-ing To its end.

Lord, Teach a Little Child to Pray

13

BROWN.   William B. Bradbury, 1840

1. Lord, teach a lit - tle child to pray, And O, ac - cept my pray'r!
2. A lit - tle spar-row can - not fall, Un - not-iced, Lord, by Thee;
3. Teach me to do what-e'er is right, And when I sin, for - give;

Thou hear - est ev - 'ry word I say, For Thou art ev - 'ry-where.
And though I am so young and small, Thou dost take care of me.
And make it still my chief de-light To love Thee while I live.

A Little Talk With Jesus

Arr.

Arr. by J. H. H.

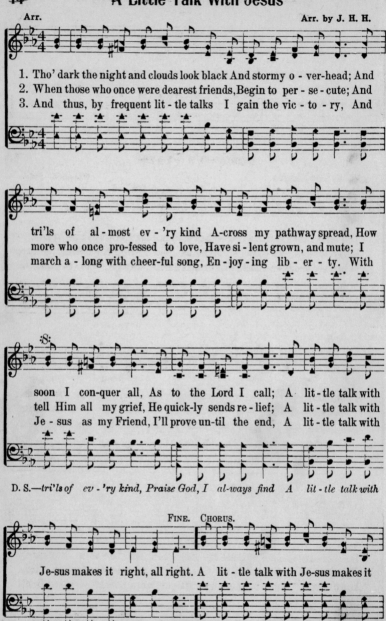

1. Tho' dark the night and clouds look black And stormy o - ver-head; And
2. When those who once were dearest friends, Begin to per - se - cute; And
3. And thus, by frequent lit - tle talks I gain the vic - to - ry, And

tri'ls of al - most ev - 'ry kind A-cross my pathway spread, How
more who once pro-fessed to love, Have si - lent grown, and mute; I
march a - long with cheer-ful song, En - joy - ing lib - er - ty. With

soon I con-quer all, As to the Lord I call; A lit - tle talk with
tell Him all my grief, He quick-ly sends re - lief; A lit - tle talk with
Je - sus as my Friend, I'll prove un-til the end, A lit - tle talk with

D. S.—*tri'ls of ev - 'ry kind, Praise God, I al-ways find A lit - tle talk with*

FINE. CHORUS.

Je-sus makes it right, all right. A lit - tle talk with Je-sus makes it

Je - sus makes it right, all right.

D. S.

right, all right; A lit-tle talk with Je-sus makes it right, all right. In

Children's Prayer

15

Elsie Byler-Burkhard

Walter E. Yoder

1. In the ear - ly morn-ing When the sunbeams bright Shine around our
2. When temptations gath - er, Fears or foes af-fright,When our footsteps
3. When the shadows lengthen, Bringing sweet re-pose, Wea - ry hands are

path - way, Scat - ter - ing the night, Je - sus, gen - tle Sav - iour,
wa - ver In the path of right, Je - sus, ten - der Sav - iour,
fold - ed, Lit - tle eye - lids close, Je - sus, lov - ing Sav - iour,

Hear our earnest pray'r; Bless the little children, Take us in Thy care.
With Thine arm uphold: All our upward strivings In Thy love en - fold.
Guard us thro' the night; Keep Thy little children Safe till morning light.

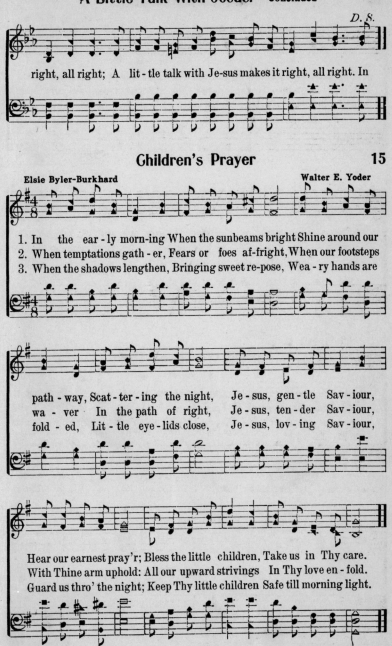

The Morning Bright

1. The morning bright, With ro - sy light, Hath waked me from my sleep;
2. All thro' the day, I humbly pray, Be Thou my Guard and Guide;
3. Oh, make Thy rest With-in my breast, Great Spir-it of all grace;

Fa - ther, I own Thy love a - lone Thy lit - tle one doth keep.
My sins for-give, And let me live, Blest Je - sus, near Thy side.
Make me like Thee, Then shall I be Prepared to see Thy face.

17

Father, We Thank Thee

1. Father, we thank Thee for the night, And for the pleasant morning light,
2. Help us to do the things we should, To be to oth - ers kind and good;

For rest and food, and lov-ing care, And all that makes the day so fair.
In all our work, and all our play, To love Thee bet-ter ev - 'ry day.

Jesus, From Thy Throne On High

T. B. Pollock

W. S. Hoyte

1. Je - sus, from Thy throne on high, Far a-bove the bright blue sky,
2. Be Thou with us ev - 'ry day, In our work and in our play,
3. May we grow from day to day, Glad to learn each ho - ly way.

Look on us with lov - ing eye, Hear us, Ho - ly Je - sus.
When we learn and when we pray; Hear us, Ho - ly Je - sus.
Ev - er read - y to o - bey: Hear us, Ho - ly Je - sus.

Sun Of My Soul

HURSLEY

Peter Ritter, 1792
Arr. by William H. Monk, 1861

John Keble, 1827

1. Sun of my soul, Thou Saviour dear, It is not night if Thou be near;
2. When the soft dews of kind-ly sleep My wea-ry eye-lids gen-tly steep,
3. A - bide with me from morn till eve, For without Thee I can-not live;
4. Watch by the sick: enrich the poor With blessings from Thy boundless store;
5. Come near and bless us when we wake, Ere thro' the world our way we take,

Oh, may no earth-born cloud a-rise To hide Thee from Thy servant's eyes.
Be my last tho't,—how sweet to rest For - ev - er on my Saviour's breast.
A - bide with me when night is nigh, For without Thee I dare not die.
Be ev'ry mourner's sleep to-night, Like infant's slumbers, pure and light.
Till, in the o - cean of Thy love, We lose ourselves in heav'n a-bove.

20 Now The Light Has Gone Away

Frances R Havergal

German

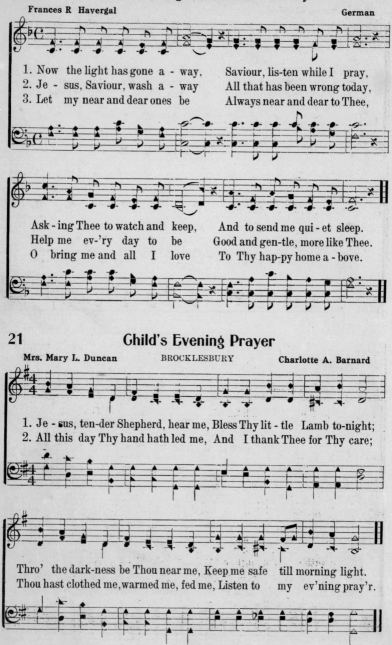

1. Now the light has gone a - way, Saviour, lis-ten while I pray,
2. Je - sus, Saviour, wash a - way All that has been wrong today,
3. Let my near and dear ones be Always near and dear to Thee,

Ask - ing Thee to watch and keep, And to send me qui - et sleep.
Help me ev-'ry day to be Good and gen-tle, more like Thee.
O bring me and all I love To Thy hap-py home a - bove.

21 Child's Evening Prayer

Mrs. Mary L. Duncan

BROCKLESBURY

Charlotte A. Barnard

1. Je - sus, ten-der Shepherd, hear me, Bless Thy lit - tle Lamb to-night;
2. All this day Thy hand hath led me, And I thank Thee for Thy care;

Thro' the dark-ness be Thou near me, Keep me safe till morning light.
Thou hast clothed me, warmed me, fed me, Listen to my ev'ning pray'r.

Evening Hymn

Sabine Baring-Gould

Joseph Barnby

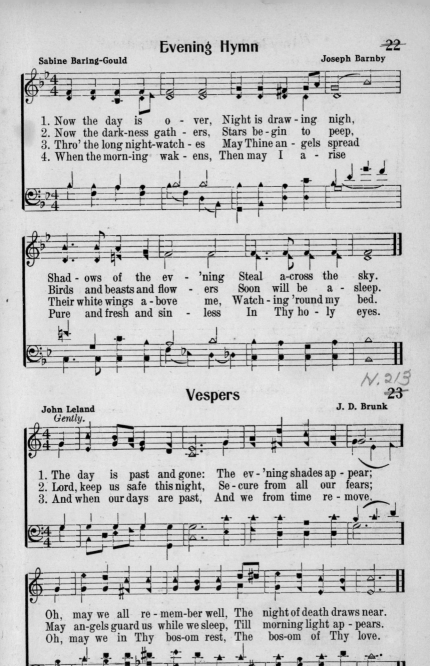

1. Now the day is o - ver, Night is draw - ing nigh,
2. Now the dark-ness gath - ers, Stars be - gin to peep,
3. Thro' the long night-watch - es May Thine an - gels spread
4. When the morn-ing wak - ens, Then may I a - rise

Shad - ows of the ev - 'ning Steal a-cross the sky.
Birds and beasts and flow - ers Soon will be a - sleep.
Their white wings a - bove me, Watch - ing 'round my bed.
Pure and fresh and sin - less In Thy ho - ly eyes.

N. 213

Vespers

John Leland
Gently.

J. D. Brunk

1. The day is past and gone: The ev - 'ning shades ap - pear;
2. Lord, keep us safe this night, Se - cure from all our fears;
3. And when our days are past, And we from time re - move.

Oh, may we all re - mem-ber well, The night of death draws near.
May an-gels guard us while we sleep, Till morning light ap - pears.
Oh, may we in Thy bos-om rest, The bos-om of Thy love.

24 Day Is Dying In The West

Mary A. Lathbury, 1841   CHAUTAUQUA   W. F. Sherwin. 1877

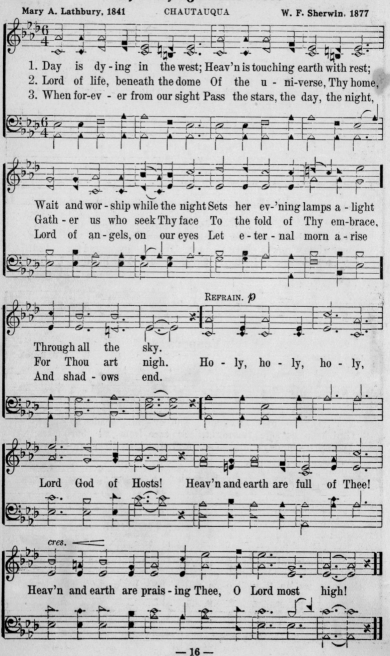

1. Day is dy-ing in the west; Heav'n is touching earth with rest;
2. Lord of life, beneath the dome Of the u-ni-verse, Thy home,
3. When for-ev - er from our sight Pass the stars, the day, the night,

Wait and wor - ship while the night Sets her ev-'ning lamps a - light
Gath - er us who seek Thy face To the fold of Thy em-brace,
Lord of an - gels, on our eyes Let e - ter - nal morn a - rise

REFRAIN. p

Through all the sky.
For Thou art nigh.   Ho - ly, ho - ly, ho - ly,
And shad - ows end.

Lord God of Hosts! Heav'n and earth are full of Thee!

cres.

Heav'n and earth are prais - ing Thee, O Lord most high!

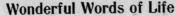

Wonderful Words of Life

P. P. B.

P. P. Bliss

25

1. Sing them o-ver a-gain to me, Won-der-ful words of Life;
2. Christ, the bless-ed One, gives to all Won-der-ful words of Life;
3. Sweet-ly ech-o the gos-pel call, Won-der-ful words of Life;

Let me more of their beau-ty see, Won-der-ful words of Life;
Sin-ner, list to the lov-ing call, Won-der-ful words of Life;
Of-fer par-don and peace to all, Won-der-ful words of Life;

Words of life and beau-ty, Teach me faith and du-ty;
All so free-ly giv-en, Woo-ing us to heav-en;
Je-sus, on-ly Sav-iour, Sanc-ti-fy for-ev-er.

REFRAIN.

Beau-ti-ful words, won-der-ful words, Won-der-ful words of Life;

Beau-ti-ful words, won-der-ful words, Won-der-ful words of Life.

My Mother's Bible

Evangelist M. B. Williams

Charlie D. Tillman

DUET.

1. There's a dear and pre-cious Book, Tho' its worn and fad-ed now,
2. There she read of Je-sus' love, As He blest the chil-dren dear,
3. Well, those days are past and gone, But their mem-'ry lin-gers still,

Which re-calls those hap-py days of long a-go,
How He suf-fered, bled and died up-on the tree;
And the dear old Book each day has been my guide;

When I stood at moth-er's knee, With her hand up-on my brow,
Of His heav-y load of care. Then she dried my flow-ing tear
And I seek to do His will, As my moth-er taught me then,

And I heard her voice in gen-tle tones and low.
With her kiss-es, as she said it was for me.
And ev-er in my heart His words a-bide.

CHORUS.

Blessed Book,..... precious Book,..... On thy dear old tear-stained
Blessed Book, precious Book,

leaves I love to look;............ Thou art
love to look;

sweet - er day by day, As I walk the nar - row way

That leads at last to that bright home a - bove.

The " Bible."

27

The B - I - B - L - E, Yes, that's the Book for me; I

stand a - lone on the Word of God, The B - I - B - L - E.

NOTE.—Let the teacher hold up a Bible and let the children point to it as they sing
"B-I-B-L-E;" or, use as a finger exercise, touching each finger as they sing "B-I-B-L-E."

No 97

Welcome Sunday Morning

Jessie Brown Pounds

Victor Herman

1. O wel-come Sun-day morn-ing, A gift from God a-bove;
2. A touch of ho-ly beau-ty It lays up-on the earth;
3. From earthly toil and pleas-ure We glad-ly turn a-way,

It comes with heav-en's warn-ing, It comes with heav-en's love.
Sweet tho'ts of love and du-ty, In hu-man hearts have birth.
To take from God this treas-ure, This ho-ly, hap-py day.

The day comes back a-gain, The gift of God to men;

The day when Je-sus rose Tri-umph-ant o'er His foes.

29 H370

Above the Trembling Elements

Mrs. Price
Slowly.

DUNDEE

Guil. Franc, 1545

1. A - bove the trembling el - e-ments, A - bove life's rest-less sea,
2. Great calmness there, sweet patience, too, Up - on Thy face I see:
3. I am not wea - ry of Thy work, From earth I would not flee;
4. That I may bless my ten - der friends, And those who love not me;
5. What-ev - er falls, of good or ill, Thy hand, Thy care I see,
6. And when my eyes close for the last, Still this my pray'r shall be,—

Above the Trembling Elements.—Concluded

Dear Sav - iour, lift my spir - it up, Oh, lift me up to Thee!
I would be calm and pa - tient, Lord, Oh, lift me up to Thee!
But while I walk, and while I serve, Oh, lift me up to Thee!
Oh, lift me high a - bove my - self, Dear Je - sus, up to Thee!
And while these var - ied deal-ings pass, Oh, lift my up to Thee!
Dear Sav - iour, lift my spir - it up, And lift me up to Thee.

Father in Heaven — 30

Adapted from Kuhlau

1. Fa - ther in heav - en, bless Thy lit - tle chil-dren, Gathered be -
2. Fa - ther in heav - en, help Thy lit - tle chil-dren To please Thee

fore Thee on this Thy ho - ly day. For the morning sun-shine,
ev - er in their work and play; Help them to be truth - ful,

for the day we thank Thee, Oh, Sun of Love, shine, shine in our hearts, we pray!
gentle, kind and lov-ing, To be like Je-sus, and fol-low Him al - way.

— 21 —

Little Children, Can You Tell?

German

Teacher.

Lit - tle chil-dren, can you tell   Who has kept us safe and well

All.

Come then, let us thank-ful be,   For His mer-cies large and free!

Through the watch - es   of   the night,   Till the morn-ing light?

Ev - 'ry morn - ing   let   us raise,   High our song of   praise.

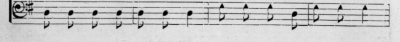

Children.

Yes,   it   is   our God doth keep,   Lit - tle chil-dren while they sleep,

All.

Praise Him for these hap - py   hours,   Praise Him for our var - ied pow'rs,

He   has kept   us   from all harm,   By His pow'r - ful   arm.

Praise Him ev - 'ry heart and voice,   While we   all   re - joice.

Our Sunday-School Is Over

Our Sun-day-school is o - ver, And we are go - ing home,

Teacher.

Good - bye, good - bye; Be al - ways kind and true;

Scholars.

Goob - bye, good - bye, We will be kind and true.

Note.—In some schools when singing "Good-by," the teachers and scholars wave the hands outwardly, first the right and then the left; or the song may be sung by the children as they march from the room.

Closing Prayer

Mary B. Blakemore

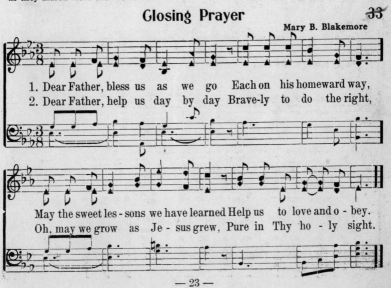

1. Dear Father, bless us as we go Each on his homeward way,
2. Dear Father, help us day by day Brave-ly to do the right,

May the sweet les - sons we have learned Help us to love and o - bey.
Oh, may we grow as Je - sus grew, Pure in Thy ho - ly sight.

The Sunday-School

1. The Sunday-school, that blessed place, Oh! I would rath-er stay
2. 'Tis there I learn that Je-sus died For sin-ners such as I;
3. Then let our grate-ful trib-ute rise, And songs of praise be giv'n
4. And welcome, then, the Sunday-school, We'll read, and sing, and pray,

Within its walls, a child of grace, Than spend my hours in play.
Oh, what has all the world be-side, That I should prize so high?
To Him who dwells a-bove the skies, For such a bless-ing giv'n.
That we may keep the gold-en rule, And nev-er from it stray.

CHORUS.

The Sunday-school, the Sunday-school, Oh! 'tis the place I love,

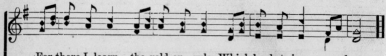

For there I learn the gold-en rule, Which leads to joys a-bove.

Hear the Pennies Dropping

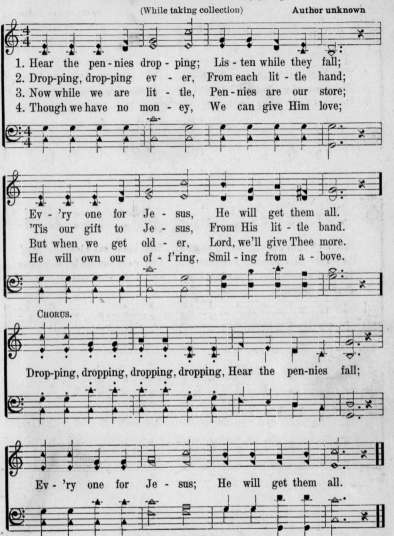

(While taking collection)

Author unknown

1. Hear the pen-nies drop-ping; Lis-ten while they fall;
2. Drop-ping, drop-ping ev-er, From each lit-tle hand;
3. Now while we are lit-tle, Pen-nies are our store;
4. Though we have no mon-ey, We can give Him love;

Ev-'ry one for Je-sus, He will get them all.
'Tis our gift to Je-sus, From His lit-tle band.
But when we get old-er, Lord, we'll give Thee more.
He will own our of-f'ring, Smil-ing from a-bove.

Chorus.

Drop-ping, dropping, dropping, dropping, Hear the pen-nies fall;

Ev - 'ry one for Je - sus; He will get them all.

Hear the Pennies Dropping

To the tune "LITTLE DROPS OF WATER"

Hear the pennies dropping;
  Listen as they fall;
Every one for Jesus,
  He will get them all.

Dropping, dropping ever,
  From each little hand;
'Tis our gift to Jesus,
  From His little band.

We Wish a Happy Birthday

E. E. Hewitt

Grant Colfax Tullar

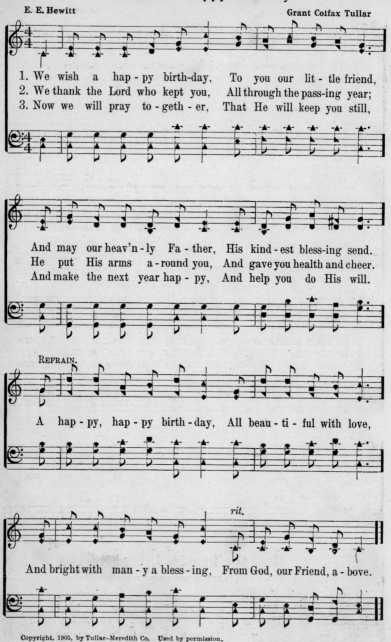

1. We wish a hap-py birth-day, To you our lit-tle friend,
2. We thank the Lord who kept you, All through the pass-ing year;
3. Now we will pray to-geth-er, That He will keep you still,

And may our heav'n-ly Fa-ther, His kind-est bless-ing send.
He put His arms a-round you, And gave you health and cheer.
And make the next year hap-py, And help you do His will.

REFRAIN.

A hap-py, hap-py birth-day, All beau-ti-ful with love,

rit.

And bright with man-y a bless-ing, From God, our Friend, a-bove.

All the Happy Children

Frances Bent Dillingham

Frances R. Havergal

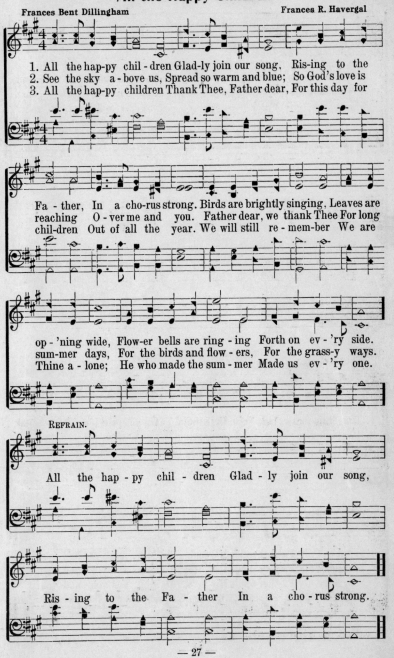

1. All the hap-py chil - dren Glad-ly join our song, Ris-ing to the
2. See the sky a - bove us, Spread so warm and blue; So God's love is
3. All the hap-py children Thank Thee, Father dear, For this day for

Fa - ther, In a cho-rus strong. Birds are brightly singing, Leaves are
reaching O - ver me and you. Father dear, we thank Thee For long
chil-dren Out of all the year. We will still re - mem-ber We are

op - 'ning wide, Flow-er bells are ring - ing Forth on ev - 'ry side.
sum-mer days, For the birds and flow - ers, For the grass-y ways.
Thine a - lone; He who made the sum - mer Made us ev - 'ry one.

REFRAIN.

All the hap - py chil - dren Glad - ly join our song,

Ris - ing to the Fa - ther In a cho - rus strong.

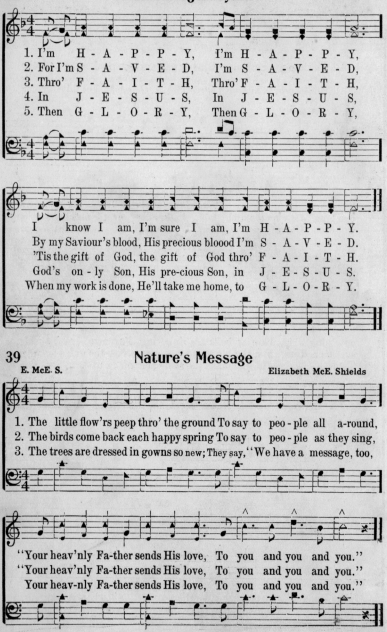

Who Made the Pretty Lilies?

Mrs. C. D. Martin

W. Stillman Martin

1. ¹Who made the pret - ty lil - ies? ²God did, God did,
2. ⁵Who loves the lit - tle chil - dren? ²God does, God does,
3. ⁴Who gave the world a Sav - iour? ²God did, God did,

¹Who made the pret - ty lil - ies? ²God did we know.
⁵Who loves the lit - tle chil - dren? ²God does we know.
⁴Who gave the world a Sav - iour? ²God did we know.

CHORUS.

²God made the ⁴lil - ies pure and white, ²God made the ³stars that

shine so bright, ²God gave the world ⁴His Life and Light, ²God did we know.

MOTIONS.—1 Point to lilies. 2 Point up, turn eyes upward. 3 Sweep right hand from right to left pointing upward. 4 Throw right hand outward. 5 Point to other children.

Little Eyes

Dr. C. R. Blackall

W. H. Doane

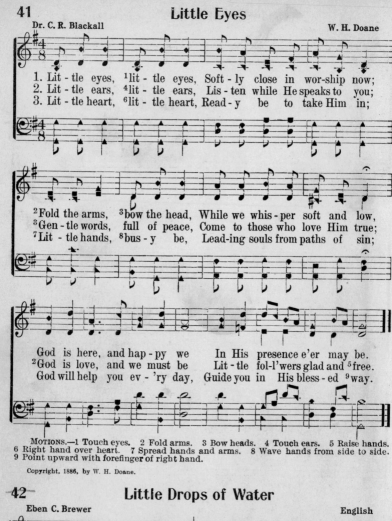

1. Lit - tle eyes, ¹lit - tle eyes, Soft - ly close in wor-ship now;
2. Lit - tle ears, ⁴lit - tle ears, Lis - ten while He speaks to you;
3. Lit - tle heart, ⁶lit - tle heart, Read - y be to take Him in;

²Fold the arms, ³bow the head, While we whis - per soft and low,
³Gen - tle words, full of peace, Come to those who love Him true;
⁷Lit - tle hands, ⁸bus - y be, Lead-ing souls from paths of sin;

God is here, and hap - py we In His presence e'er may be.
²God is love, and we must be Lit - tle fol-l'wers glad and ⁵free.
God will help you ev - 'ry day, Guide you in His bless - ed ⁹way.

MOTIONS.—1 Touch eyes. 2 Fold arms. 3 Bow heads. 4 Touch ears. 5 Raise hands.
6 Right hand over heart. 7 Spread hands and arms. 8 Wave hands from side to side.
9 Point upward with forefinger of right hand.

42   Little Drops of Water

Eben C. Brewer

English

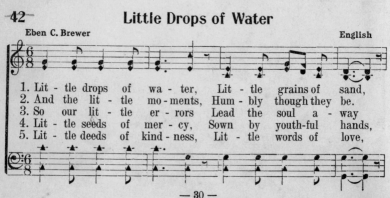

1. Lit - tle drops of wa - ter, Lit - tle grains of sand,
2. And the lit - tle mo - ments, Hum - bly though they be.
3. So our lit - tle er - rors Lead the soul a - way
4. Lit - tle seeds of mer - cy, Sown by youth-ful hands,
5. Lit - tle deeds of kind - ness, Lit - tle words of love,

Little Drops of Water.—Concluded

Make the might-y o-cean, And the pleasant land.
Make the might-y a-ges Of e-ter-ni-ty.
From the path of vir-tue Oft in sin to stray.
Grow to bless the na-tions Far in heathen lands.
Make our earth an e-den Like the heav'n a-bove.

Sun and Rain

43

A. A. Payn

Herbert J. Lacey

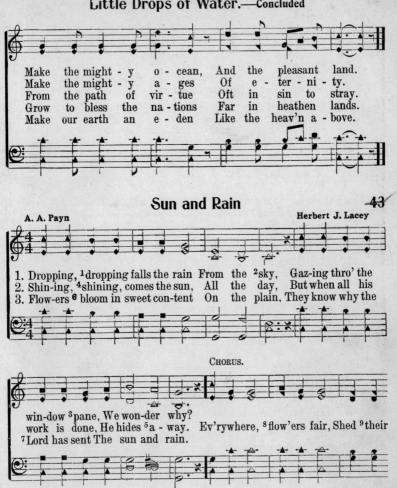

1. Dropping, [1]dropping falls the rain From the [2]sky, Gaz-ing thro' the
2. Shin-ing, [4]shining, comes the sun, All the day, But when all his
3. Flow-ers [6] bloom in sweet con-tent On the plain, They know why the

CHORUS.

win-dow [3]pane, We won-der why?
work is done, He hides [5]a - way. Ev'rywhere, [8]flow'rs fair, Shed [9]their
[7]Lord has sent The sun and rain.

fragrance on the air Ev-'ry day, praising [10]Him for [11]His care.

GESTURES.—1 Raise hands, bring down, moving fingers. 2 Look up. 3 Hand over eyes as if gazing. 4 Both hands extended out and up. 5 Cover eyes with both hands. 6 Both hands extended, wave to and fro, palms down. 7 Look up. 8 Arms stretched out from side. 9 Point down with left hand. 10 Point up with right hand. 11 Bring hands down.

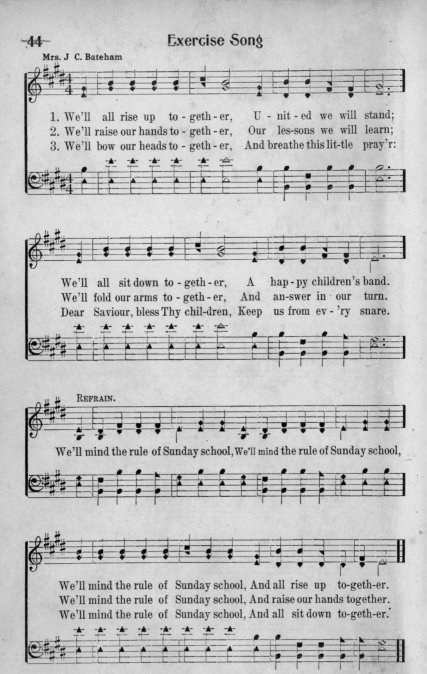

44 **Exercise Song**

Mrs. J C. Bateham

1. We'll all rise up to-geth-er, U-nit-ed we will stand;
2. We'll raise our hands to-geth-er, Our les-sons we will learn;
3. We'll bow our heads to-geth-er, And breathe this lit-tle pray'r:

We'll all sit down to-geth-er, A hap-py children's band.
We'll fold our arms to-geth-er, And an-swer in our turn.
Dear Saviour, bless Thy chil-dren, Keep us from ev-'ry snare.

REFRAIN.

We'll mind the rule of Sunday school, We'll mind the rule of Sunday school,

We'll mind the rule of Sunday school, And all rise up to-geth-er.
We'll mind the rule of Sunday school, And raise our hands together.
We'll mind the rule of Sunday school, And all sit down to-geth-er.

Two Little Hands

W. A. O.

W. A. Ogden

1. I've two lit-tle hands to work for Je-sus, One lit-tle tongue His
2. I've two lit-tle feet to tread the path-way Up to the heav'nly
3. I've one lit-tle heart to give to Je-sus, One lit-tle soul for

praise to tell, Two lit-tle ears to hear His coun-sel,
courts a-bove; Two lit-tle eyes to read the Bi-ble,
Him to save, One lit-tle life for His dear serv-ice,

CHORUS.

One lit-tle voice a song to swell.
Tell-ing of Je-sus' wondrous love. Lord, we come, Lord, we come,
One lit-tle self that He must have.

1
2

In our childhood's ear-ly morn-ing; Come to learn of Thee.

God, Make My Life a Little Light

C. E. Pollock

1. God, make my life a lit-tle light, With-in the world to glow;
2. God, make my life a lit-tle flow'r, That giv-eth joy to all;
3. God, make my life a lit-tle song, That com-fort-eth the sad;
4. God, make my life a lit-tle hymn, Of ten-der-ness and praise;

A lit-tle flame that burneth bright Wher-ev-er I may go.
Con-tent to bloom in na-tive bow'r Although its place be small.
That help-eth oth-ers to be strong, And makes the sing-er glad.
Of faith that nev-er wax-eth dim—In all His wondrous ways.

CHORUS.

Lit-tle light, lit-tle light, Wher-ev-er I may go;
Lit-tle light, lit-tle light,

lit-tle light, lit-tle light, Wher-ev-er I may go.
Lit-tle light, lit-tle light,

Shine Where You Are

C. H. G.

Chas. H. Gabriel

1. Be a shining light, Radiant, clear and bright, Like a brilliant, sil -
2. Keep your lamp a - trim, Let it ne'er grow dim—Let it gleam and glow
3. Go to those in need, And by kind - ly deed Spread the gos-pel mes -

ver - y star; Sing a cheer - y song As you pass a - long,
like a star. Flood your path with cheer When the way grows drear,
sage a - far. Small tho' be your field, Great may be its yield—

CHORUS.

Shine for Je - sus, and shine where you are. Shine where you are,

Shine like a star! Send out your light near and far; When you

meet the test, Do your ver - y best, Shine for Jesus, and shine where you are.

Sunbeams For Jesus

Grace Gordon

Howard E. Smith

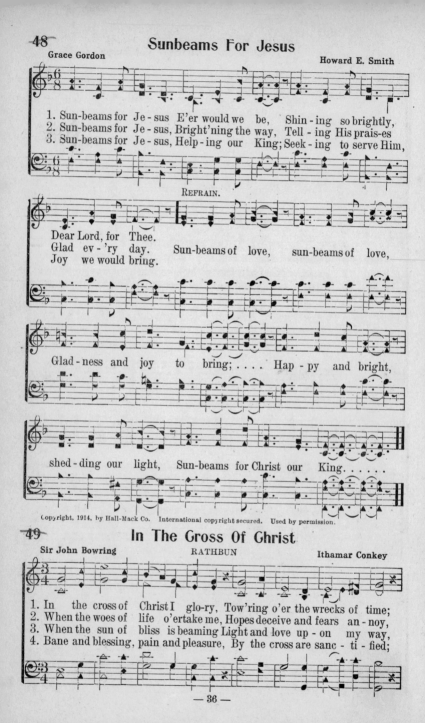

1. Sun-beams for Je-sus E'er would we be, Shin-ing so brightly,
2. Sun-beams for Je-sus, Bright'ning the way, Tell-ing His prais-es
3. Sun-beams for Je-sus, Help-ing our King; Seek-ing to serve Him,

REFRAIN.

Dear Lord, for Thee.
Glad ev-'ry day. Sun-beams of love, sun-beams of love,
Joy we would bring.

Glad-ness and joy to bring;.... Hap-py and bright,

shed-ding our light, Sun-beams for Christ our King......

In The Cross Of Christ

Sir John Bowring

RATHBUN

Ithamar Conkey

1. In the cross of Christ I glo-ry, Tow'ring o'er the wrecks of time;
2. When the woes of life o'ertake me, Hopes deceive and fears an-noy,
3. When the sun of bliss is beaming Light and love up-on my way,
4. Bane and blessing, pain and pleasure, By the cross are sanc-ti-fied;

In The Cross Of Christ—Concluded

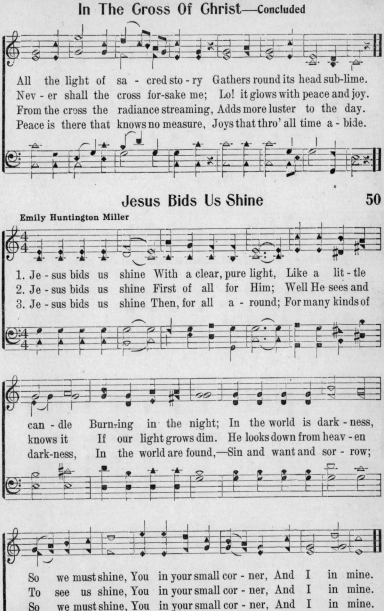

All the light of sa - cred sto - ry Gathers round its head sub-lime.
Nev - er shall the cross for-sake me; Lo! it glows with peace and joy.
From the cross the radiance streaming, Adds more luster to the day.
Peace is there that knows no measure, Joys that thro' all time a - bide.

Jesus Bids Us Shine

50

Emily Huntington Miller

1. Je - sus bids us shine With a clear, pure light, Like a lit - tle
2. Je - sus bids us shine First of all for Him; Well He sees and
3. Je - sus bids us shine Then, for all a - round; For many kinds of

can - dle Burn-ing in the night; In the world is dark - ness,
knows it If our light grows dim. He looks down from heav - en
dark-ness, In the world are found,—Sin and want and sor - row;

So we must shine, You in your small cor - ner, And I in mine.
To see us shine, You in your small cor - ner, And I in mine.
So we must shine, You in your small cor - ner, And I in mine.

51 Light Of The World

Elsie Duncan Yale

Herbert J. Lacy

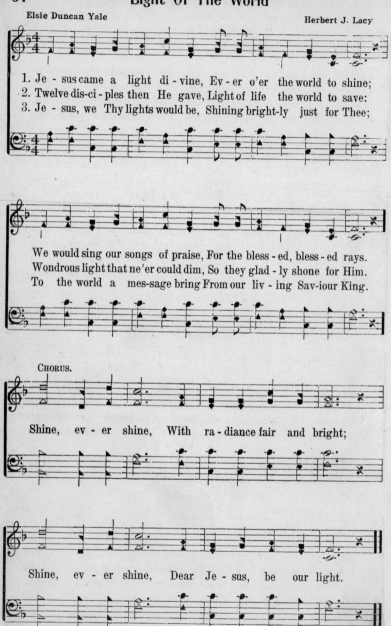

1. Je - sus came a light di - vine, Ev - er o'er the world to shine;
2. Twelve dis-ci - ples then He gave, Light of life the world to save:
3. Je - sus, we Thy lights would be, Shining bright-ly just for Thee;

We would sing our songs of praise, For the bless - ed, bless - ed rays.
Wondrous light that ne'er could dim, So they glad - ly shone for Him.
To the world a mes-sage bring From our liv - ing Sav-iour King.

CHORUS.

Shine, ev - er shine, With ra - diance fair and bright;

Shine, ev - er shine, Dear Je - sus, be our light.

Stand Up, Stand Up for Jesus

52

George Duffield, Jr., 1858   WEBB   George J. Webb, 1837

1. Stand up, stand up for Je - sus! Ye sol- diers of the cross;
2. Stand up, stand up for Je - sus! The trum-pet call o - bey;
3. Stand up, stand up for Je - sus! Stand in His strength a - lone;
4. Stand up, stand up for Je - sus! The strife will not be long;

Lift high His roy - al ban - ner, It must not suf - fer loss:
Forth to the might-y con - flict, In this His glo-rious day:
The arm of flesh will fail you; Ye dare not trust your own:
This day the noise of bat - tle, The next the vic-tor's song:

From vic - t'ry un - to vic - t'ry His ar - my shall He lead,
Ye that are men, now serve Him, A-gainst un-num-bered foes;
Put on the gos - pel ar - mor, And, watching un - to pray'r;
To him that o - ver - com - eth, A crown of life shall be;

Till ev - 'ry foe is vanquished And Christ is Lord in - deed.
Your cour - age rise with dan - ger, And strength to strength oppose.
Where du - ty calls, or dan - ger, Be nev - er want - ing there.
He with the King of glo - ry Shall reign e - ter - nal - ly.

Toiling for Jesus

W. A. O

W. A. Ogden

Spirited.

1. Bright-ly, sweet-ly, toil-ing for the Mas-ter, Go we forth with will-ing hands to do What-so-e'er to us He hath ap-point-ed, Faith-ful-ly our mis-sion to pur-sue. Toil - ing for Je - sus, Joy-ful-ly we go, joy-ful-ly we go; Toil - ing for Je - sus, In His vineyard here be - low.

2. Glad-ly, sweet-ly, we will tell the sto - ry Of His love to mor-tals here be - low; Christ, the brightness of the Father's glo-ry, Free - ly here His bless-ing will be-stow.

3. Meek-ly, meek-ly, toil-ing for the Mas-ter, Walk-ing faith-ful-ly the path He trod; Lead-ing wand'rers to the dear Re-deem-er, Point-ing sin-ners to the Lamb of God.

CHORUS.

Toil - ing, toil - ing for the Mas - ter, yes, Toil-ing, toil-ing for the Mas - ter,

Knowles Shaw

George A. Minor

1. Sowing in the morn-ing, sowing seeds of kind-ness, Sowing in the noon-tide
2. Sowing in she sunshine, sowing in the shad-ows, Fearing neith-er clouds nor
3. Go-ing forth with weeping, sowing for the Mas-ter, Tho' the loss sustained our

and the dew - y eve; Wait-ing for the har - vest, And the time of reap - ing,
winter's chill-ing breeze; By and by the har - vest, And the la - bor end - ed,
spir - it oft-en grieves; When our weeping's o - ver, He will bid us wel-come,

CHORUS.

We shall come, re-joic-ing, bringing in the sheaves. Bringing in the sheaves, bringing

in the sheaves, We shall come, rejoicing, bringing in the sheaves; Bringing in the sheaves,

bring-ing in the sheaves, We shall come, re-joic - ing, Bring-ing in the sheaves,

55 Work, for the Night is Coming

Anna L. Coghill

Lowell Mason

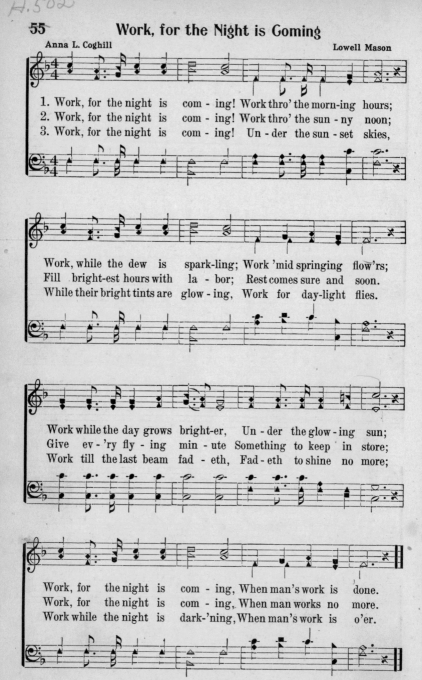

1. Work, for the night is com - ing! Work thro' the morn-ing hours;
2. Work, for the night is com - ing! Work thro' the sun - ny noon;
3. Work, for the night is com - ing! Un - der the sun - set skies,

Work, while the dew is spark-ling; Work 'mid springing flow'rs;
Fill bright-est hours with la - bor; Rest comes sure and soon.
While their bright tints are glow - ing, Work for day-light flies.

Work while the day grows bright-er, Un - der the glow - ing sun;
Give ev - 'ry fly - ing min - ute Something to keep in store;
Work till the last beam fad - eth, Fad - eth to shine no more;

Work, for the night is com - ing, When man's work is done.
Work, for the night is com - ing, When man works no more.
Work while the night is dark-'ning, When man's work is o'er.

Good Cheer Song

Mrs. C. D. Martin   W. Stillman Martin

1. Ev - 'ry-bod - y- needs a lit - tle sun - shine, Ev - 'ry-bod - y
2. Ev - 'ry-bod - y needs a lit - tle kind - ness, Ev - 'ry-bod - y
3. Ev - 'ry-bod - y needs a life a - bun-dant, Needs the health and

needs a lov-ing Friend; Ev-'ry-bod - y sometimes gets dis-cour - aged,
needs to know the Lord; Needs the strength that faith in Christ can give them,
hap-pi-ness of heav'n, Needs the blood of Christ to cleanse and save them,

CHORUS.

Longs for kindness you could well ex - tend.
Needs the bless-ed light of His pure Word. Just a lit - tle sunshine
Needs the Ho - ly Spir - it God has giv'n.

bright'ning up the way, Just a little good cheer scattered ev'ry day, Bringing heaven

near-er, Making du-ty clearer, Making life seem dearer, While we toil or play.

57 Higher Still, and Higher

E. E. Hewitt

Grant Colfax Tullar

1. The lit - tle trees are grow - ing, Out in the for - est wild;
2. The lit - tle vines are climb - ing, Still high - er in the light:
3. O, like. the dear child Je - sus, May we, from day to day,

They tell a hap - py sto - ry To ev - 'ry lit - tle child.
They grow in rain and sun - shine, More beau-ti - ful and bright.
In grace and good-ness grow - ing, The Father's Word o - bey.

REFRAIN.

High - er still, and high - er, We'll be ris - ing, too;

Learn-ing more of Je - sus, Les - sons sweet and true.

Copyright, 1905, by Tullar–Meredith Co. Used by permission.

58 Children of the Heavenly King

John Cennick, 1742

PLEYEL'S HYMN

Arr. from Ignaz J. Pleyel, 1790

1. Chil-dren of the heav'nly King, As we jour - ney, sweetly sing;
2. We are trav'ling home to God In the way the father's trod;
3. Fear not, brethren; joy - ful stand On the bor - ders of your land;
4. Lord, o - be - dient-ly we go, Glad-ly leav - ing all be - low;

— 44 —

Children of the Heavenly King—Concluded

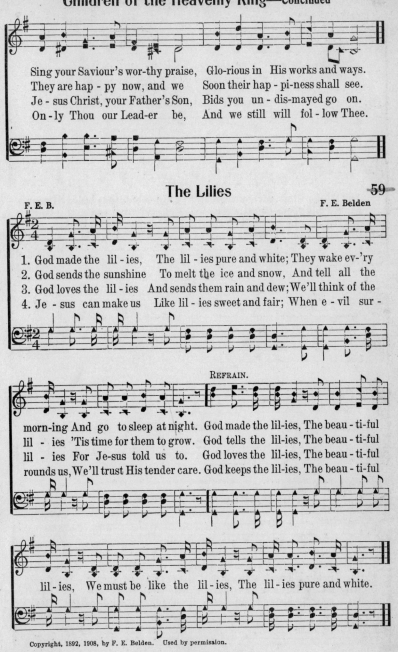

Sing your Saviour's wor-thy praise, Glo-rious in His works and ways.
They are hap - py now, and we Soon their hap - pi-ness shall see.
Je - sus Christ, your Father's Son, Bids you un - dis-mayed go on.
On - ly Thou our Lead-er be, And we still will fol - low Thee.

The Lilies

59

F. E. B.

F. E. Belden

1. God made the lil - ies, The lil - ies pure and white; They wake ev-'ry
2. God sends the sunshine To melt the ice and snow, And tell all the
3. God loves the lil - ies And sends them rain and dew; We'll think of the
4. Je - sus can make us Like lil - ies sweet and fair; When e - vil sur -

REFRAIN.

morn-ing And go to sleep at night. God made the lil-ies, The beau - ti-ful
lil - ies 'Tis time for them to grow. God tells the lil-ies, The beau - ti-ful
lil - ies For Je-sus told us to. God loves the lil-ies, The beau - ti-ful
rounds us, We'll trust His tender care. God keeps the lil-ies, The beau - ti-ful

lil - ies, We must be like the lil - ies, The lil - ies pure and white.

60 In the Temple

Flora Kirkland

Howard E. Smith

1. In the tem-ple, in the tem-ple Stood a lit-tle boy one day,
2. It was Je-sus who was teaching, And they listened to His word,
3. With the teachers there they found Him, Tho' a low-ly, learning youth,
4. "Let us ev-er then be loy-al To our God, and church, and home."

And the doc-tors wondered greatly At the words they heard Him say.
As He told them of His mis-sion From the great and mighty Lord.
But His an-swers as He told them Were complete with Bi-ble truth.
Ev-er faith-ful, ev-er trust-ing, "Nev-er minding what may come."

CHORUS.
rit

It was Je-sus! It was Je-sus! He was but a lit-tle child,

rit.

But the light of heav'n was shin-ing In His face so pure and mild.

Copyright, 1921, by Hall-Mack Co. International copyright secured. Used by permission.

61 How Gentle God's Commands

Philip Doddridge

DENNIS

Johann G. Nægeli
Adapted by L. Mason, 1845

1. How gen-tle God's commands! How kind His pre-cepts are!
2. Be-neath His watchful eye His saints se-cure-ly dwell;
3. Why should this anx-ious load Press down your wea-ry mind?
4. His good-ness stands approved, Un-changed from day to day;

— 46 —

How Gentle God's Commands—Concluded

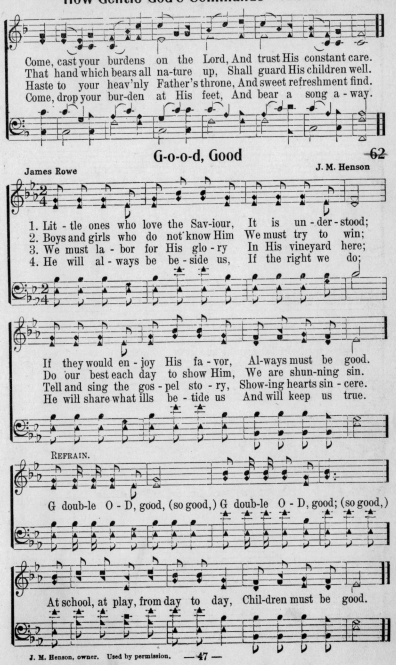

Come, cast your burdens on the Lord, And trust His constant care.
That hand which bears all na-ture up, Shall guard His children well.
Haste to your heav'nly Father's throne, And sweet refreshment find.
Come, drop your bur-den at His feet, And bear a song a-way.

G-o-o-d, Good

62

James Rowe

J. M. Henson

1. Lit - tle ones who love the Sav-iour, It is un - der - stood;
2. Boys and girls who do not know Him We must try to win;
3. We must la - bor for His glo - ry In His vineyard here;
4. He will al - ways be be - side us, If the right we do;

If they would en - joy His fa - vor, Al-ways must be good.
Do our best each day to show Him, We are shun-ning sin.
Tell and sing the gos - pel sto - ry, Show-ing hearts sin - cere.
He will share what ills be - tide us And will keep us true.

REFRAIN.

G doub-le O - D, good, (so good,) G doub-le O - D, good; (so good,)

At school, at play, from day to day, Chil-dren must be good.

63 Father, Make Us Loving

Flora Kirkland

Prayerfully.

I. H. Meredith

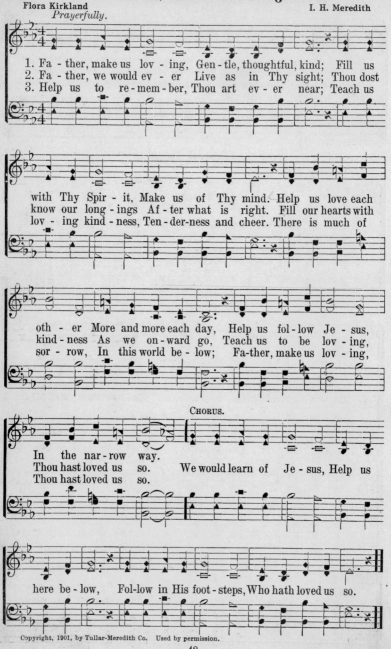

1. Fa - ther, make us lov - ing, Gen - tle, thoughtful, kind; Fill us
2. Fa - ther, we would ev - er Live as in Thy sight; Thou dost
3. Help us to re - mem - ber, Thou art ev - er near; Teach us

with Thy Spir - it, Make us of Thy mind. Help us love each
know our long - ings Af - ter what is right. Fill our hearts with
lov - ing kind - ness, Ten - der-ness and cheer. There is much of

oth - er More and more each day, Help us fol - low Je - sus,
kind - ness As we on - ward go, Teach us to be lov - ing,
sor - row, In this world be - low; Fa-ther, make us lov - ing,

CHORUS.

In the nar - row way.
Thou hast loved us so.   We would learn of Je - sus, Help us
Thou hast loved us so.

here be - low, Fol-low in His foot - steps, Who hath loved us so.

Copyright, 1901, by Tullar-Meredith Co.   Used by permission.

— 48 —

Angry Words! O Let Them Never

D. K. P.

H. R. Palmer

1. An-gry words! O let them nev-er From the tongue un-bri-dled slip;
2. Love is much too pure and ho-ly, Friendship is too sa-cred far,
3. An-gry words are light-ly spo-ken, Bitt'rest tho'ts are rash-ly stirred,

May the heart's best impulse ev-er Check them ere they soil the lip.
For a moment's reckless fol-ly Thus to des-o-late and mar.
Brightest links of life are bro-ken By a sin-gle an-gry word.

CHORUS.

"Love one an-oth-er"' thus saith the Sav-iour; Children, o-
"Love each oth-er, love each oth-er,"

bey the Fa-ther's blest command. "Love one an-oth-er,"
'tis the Fa-ther's blest com-mand. "Love each oth-

thus saith the Sav-iour; Children, o-bey His blest com-mand.
er, love each oth-er," 'Tis His blest com-mand.

65 Dare to Be a Daniel

P. P. B.

P. P. Bliss

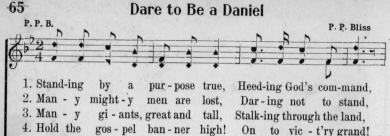

1. Stand-ing by a pur-pose true, Heed-ing God's com-mand,
2. Man-y might-y men are lost, Dar-ing not to stand,
3. Man-y gi-ants, great and tall, Stalk-ing through the land,
4. Hold the gos-pel ban-ner high! On to vic-t'ry grand!

Hon-or them, the faith-ful few! All hail to Dan-iel's Band!
Who for God had been a host, By join-ing Dan-iel's Band!
Headlong to the earth would fall, If met by Dan-iel's Band!
Sa-tan and his host de-fy, And shout for Dan-iel's Band!

CHORUS.

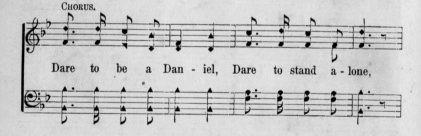

Dare to be a Dan-iel, Dare to stand a-lone,

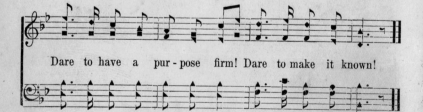

Dare to have a pur-pose firm! Dare to make it known!

Jesus Loves Even Me

P. P. B.

P. P. Bliss

1. I am so glad that our Fa-ther in heav'n Tells of His
2. Tho' I for-get Him and wan-der a-way, Still He doth
3. Oh, if there's on-ly one song I can sing, When in His

love in the Book He has giv'n, Won-der-ful things in the
love me wher-ev-er I stray; Back to His dear lov-ing
beau-ty I see the great King, This shall my song in e-

Bi-ble I see; This is the dear-est, that Je-sus loves me.
arms would I flee, When I re-mem-ber, that Je-sus loves me.
ter-ni-ty be: "Oh, what a won-der that Je-sus loves me."

REFRAIN.

I am so glad that Je-sus love me, Je-sus loves me, Je-sus loves me,

I am so glad that Je-sus loves me, Je-sus loves e-ven me.

That Sweet Story of Old

67

Mrs. Jemima Luke   DAVENANT   Old Melody

1. I think when I read that sweet sto-ry of old, When
2. Yet still to His foot-stool in pray'r I may go, And

Je-sus was here a-mong men, How He called lit-tle chil-dren as
ask for a share in His love; And if I now earn-est-ly

lambs to His fold, I should like to have been with them then.
seek Him be-low, I shall see Him and hear Him a-bove.

I wish that His hands had been placed on my head, His
In that beau-ti-ful place He has gone to pre-pare For

arms had been thrown around me, And that I might have seen His kind
all who are washed and for-giv'n; And ma-ny dear chil-dren are

-52-

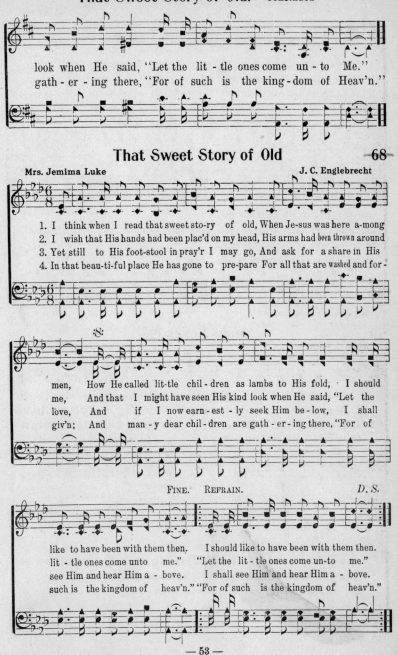

look when He said, "Let the lit - tle ones come un - to Me."
gath - er - ing there, "For of such is the king - dom of Heav'n."

That Sweet Story of Old 68

Mrs. Jemima Luke

J. C. Englebrecht

1. I think when I read that sweet sto - ry of old, When Je-sus was here a-mong
2. I wish that His hands had been plac'd on my head, His arms had been thrown around
3. Yet still to His foot-stool in pray'r I may go, And ask for a share in His
4. In that beau-ti-ful place He has gone to pre-pare For all that are washed and for -

men, How He called lit-tle chil - dren as lambs to His fold, I should
me, And that I might have seen His kind look when He said, "Let the
love, And if I now earn - est - ly seek Him be - low, I shall
giv'n; And man - y dear chil - dren are gath - er - ing there, "For of

Fine. Refrain. D. S.

like to have been with them then. I should like to have been with them then.
lit - tle ones come unto me." "Let the lit - tle ones come un-to me."
see Him and hear Him a - bove. I shall see Him and hear Him a - bove.
such is the kingdom of heav'n." "For of such is the kingdom of heav'n."

69 Little Ones Like Me

Geo. B. Holsinger

1. Je-sus, when He left the sky, And for sinners came to die, In His mercy
2. Mothers then the Saviour sought, In the places where He taught, Unto Him their
3. Did the Saviour say them nay? No, He kindly bade them stay; Suffered none to
4. Children, then, should love Him now, Strive His holy will to do, Pray to Him, and

FINE.   REFRAIN.   D. S.

passed not by Little ones like me.

children bro't, Little ones like me. Little ones like me, Little ones like me;

turn a-way Little ones like me.

praise Him too, Little ones like me.

By permission Reubush-Kieffer Co.

70 Jesus Loves Me

Anna B. Warner   Wm. B. Bradbury

1. Je-sus loves me! This I know, For the Bi-ble tells me so; Lit-tle
2. Je-sus loves me! He who died Heaven's gate to o-pen wide! He will
3. Je-sus loves me! Loves me still! Tho' I'm ver-y weak and ill; From His
4. Je-sus loves me! He will stay Close be-side me all the way; If I

REFRAIN.

ones to Him belong, They are weak, but He is strong.

wash a-way my sin, Let His lit-tle child come in. Yes, Jesus loves me!

shining home on high, Comes to watch me where I lie.

love Him, when I die He will take me home on high.

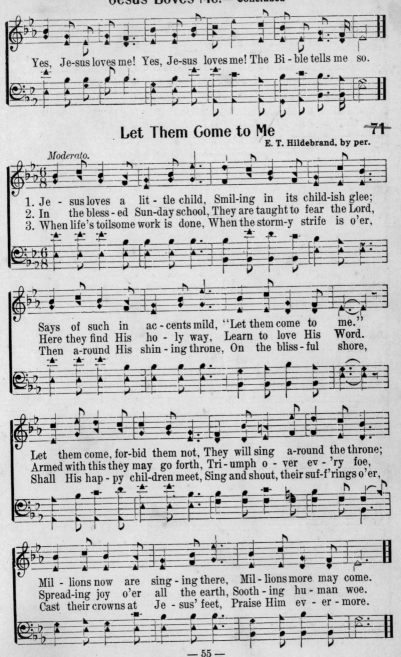

Yes, Je-sus loves me! Yes, Je-sus loves me! The Bi-ble tells me so.

Let Them Come to Me

71

E. T. Hildebrand, by per.

Moderato.

1. Je - sus loves a lit - tle child, Smil-ing in its child-ish glee;
2. In the bless - ed Sun-day school, They are taught to fear the Lord,
3. When life's toilsome work is done, When the storm-y strife is o'er,

Says of such in ac - cents mild, "Let them come to me."
Here they find His ho - ly way, Learn to love His Word.
Then a-round His shin - ing throne, On the bliss - ful shore,

Let them come, for-bid them not, They will sing a-round the throne;
Armed with this they may go forth, Tri - umph o - ver ev - 'ry foe,
Shall His hap - py chil-dren meet, Sing and shout, their suf-f'rings o'er,

Mil - lions now are sing - ing there, Mil - lions more may come.
Spread-ing joy o'er all the earth, Sooth - ing hu - man woe.
Cast their crowns at Je - sus' feet, Praise Him ev - er - more.

Jesus Calls Me

A. A. P.

A. A. Payn

1. Sweet is the voice of a moth - er, Call - ing so
2. Fair are the flow - ers that blos - som Out in the
3. Glad - ly to Him I am com - ing, All un - to

ten - der - ly, ... Sweet - er the voice of the Sav -
mead-ow free, ... Fair - er the face of my Sav -
Him I'll give, ... Will - ing - ly walk in His foot -

CHORUS.

iour, Say-ing, "O come to Me."
iour When He is call - ing me. I am so glad that He
steps, Serv-ing Him while I live.

loves me, Je - sus loves me, Je - sus loves me; I am so

glad that He calls me, For - ev - er His child to be.

God Sees the Little Sparrow Fall

Maria Straub

S. W. Straub

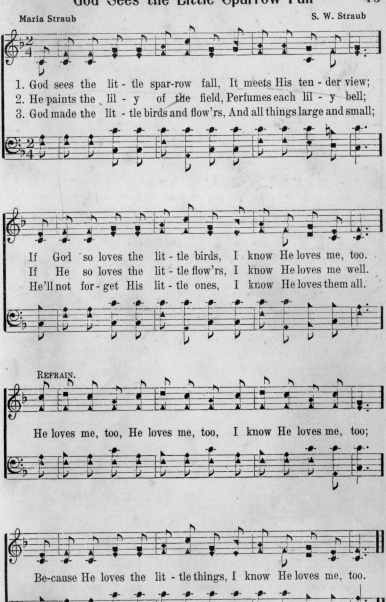

1. God sees the lit - tle spar-row fall, It meets His ten - der view;
2. He paints the lil - y of the field, Perfumes each lil - y bell;
3. God made the lit - tle birds and flow'rs, And all things large and small;

If God so loves the lit - tle birds, I know He loves me, too.
If He so loves the lit - tle flow'rs, I know He loves me well.
He'll not for - get His lit - tle ones, I know He loves them all.

REFRAIN.

He loves me, too, He loves me, too, I know He loves me, too;

Be-cause He loves the lit - tle things, I know He loves me, too.

74 We are Little Lambs

W. H. R.

W. H. Ruebush

1. We are lambs of Je-sus, and our hearts their tribute bring, We are
2. We are lambs of Je-sus, 'twas for such His life He gave, We are
3. We are lambs of Je-sus, ev-'ry foot-step He will guide, We are

precious lit-tle lambs, we are precious lit-tle lambs, And our voic-es
precious lit-tle lambs, we are precious lit-tle lambs, To re-claim the
precious lit-tle lambs, we are precious lit-tle lambs, We shall meet the

raise thanksgiving to our Lord and King, We are lambs, little lambs, precious
lost ones, all the little lambs to save, We are lambs, little lambs, precious
Shep-herd, in His sheepfold e'er a-bide, We are lambs, little lambs, precious

CHORUS.

lambs. We are lit-tle lambs, we are precious lambs, We are
precious lambs.

lit - tle lambs, we are precious lit - tle lambs, we are lit - tle lambs,

We are Little Lambs.—Concluded

we are precious lambs, We are lambs, little lambs, precious lambs.

precious lambs.

I Love to Hear the Story

75

Emily Huntington Miller

Geo. F. Root

1. I love to hear the sto - ry Which an - gel voic - es tell,
2. I'm glad my bless - ed Sav - iour Was once a child like me,
3. To sing His love and mer - cy My sweet-est song I'll raise;

How once the King of Glo - ry Came down on earth to dwell.
To show how pure and ho - ly His lit - tle ones might be;
And though I can - not see Him, I know He hears my praise;

I am both weak and sin - ful, But this I sure - ly know:
And if I try to fol - low His foot-steps here be - low,
For He has kind - ly promised That I shall sure - ly go

The Lord came down to save me Be - cause He loved me so.
He nev - er will for - get me Be - cause He loved me so.
To sing a - mong His an - gels, Be - cause He loved me so,

The Children's Friend is Jesus

R. H.

Robert Harkness

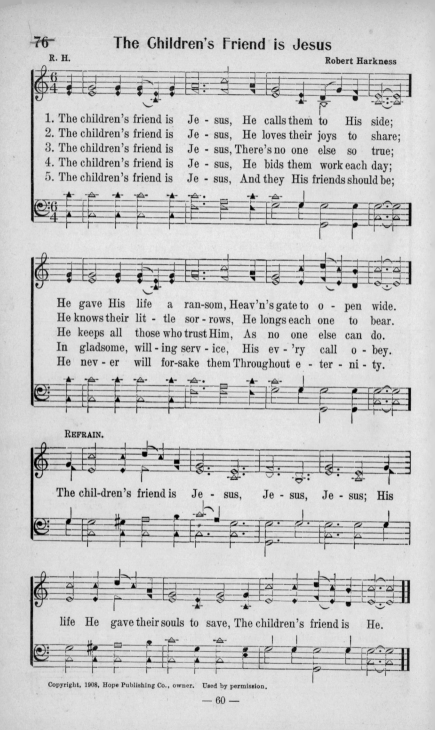

1. The children's friend is Je-sus, He calls them to His side;
2. The children's friend is Je-sus, He loves their joys to share;
3. The children's friend is Je-sus, There's no one else so true;
4. The children's friend is Je-sus, He bids them work each day;
5. The children's friend is Je-sus, And they His friends should be;

He gave His life a ran-som, Heav'n's gate to o-pen wide.
He knows their lit-tle sor-rows, He longs each one to bear.
He keeps all those who trust Him, As no one else can do.
In gladsome, will-ing serv-ice, His ev-'ry call o-bey.
He nev-er will for-sake them Throughout e-ter-ni-ty.

REFRAIN.

The chil-dren's friend is Je-sus, Je-sus, Je-sus; His

life He gave their souls to save, The children's friend is He.

Sweetly Sing the Love of Jesus

Carrie B. Adams

1. Sweet-ly sing the love of Je-sus, Love for you and
2. Glad-ly sing the love of Je-sus! Let us lean up-

love for me; Heaven's light is not more cheering, Heav-en's
on His arm; If He love us, what can grieve us? If He

dews are not more free. As a child in pain or ter-ror,
keep us, what can harm? Still He lays His hands in bless-ing

Hides him in his moth-er's breast, As a sail-or
On each tim-id lit-tle face, And in heav'n the

seeks the ha-ven, We would come to Him for rest.
chil-dren's an-gels Near the throne have al-ways place.

78   He Cares for Me

Norse Lullaby

1. How strong and sweet my Fa-ther's care, That round a-bout me,
2. Oh, keep me ev - er in Thy love, Dear Fa - ther, watch-ing

like the air, Is with me al - ways, ev - 'ry-where, Is
from a - bove, And let me still Thy mer - cy prove, And

with me al - ways, ev - 'ry-where! He cares for me.
let me still Thy mer - cy prove, And care for me.

79   Gracious Saviour, Gentle Shepherd

ST. SYLVESTER.

Miss Jane E. Lesson, (1815—1882)   John B. Dykes, (1823—1876) 1861

1. Gra - cious Sav - iour, gen - tle Shep - herd, Lit - tle
2. Ten - der Shep - herd, nev - er leave us From Thy
3. Taught to lisp the ho - ly prais - es Which on

ones are dear to Thee; Gath-ered with Thine arms, and
fold to go a - stray; By Thy look of love di -
earth Thy chil-dren sing, May we with Thy saints in

car - ried In Thy bo - som may we be.
rect - ed May we walk the nar - row way.
glo - ry Join to praise our Lord and King.

Jewels

80

W. O. Cushing

Geo. F. Root

1. When He com-eth, when He com-eth To make up His jew - els,
2. He will gath - er, He will gath - er The gems for His king - dom;
3. Lit - tle chil-dren, lit - tle chil-dren, Who love their Re-deem - er,

All His jew - els, pre-cious jew - els, His loved and His own.
All the pure ones, all the bright ones, His loved und His own.
Are the jew - els, precious jew - els, His loved and His own.

REFRAIN.

Like the stars of the morn-ing, His bright crown a - dorn - ing,

They shall shine in their beau - ty, Bright gems for His crown.

81 Children, Come

Elsie Duncan Yale

C. Austin Miles

1. I'm glad that He cares for the chil-dren, The Sav-iour so
2. For though the dis-ci-ples for-bade them, He sent not the
3. I'm glad that He welcomes the chil-dren, I know He is

lov-ing, so kind, For lo, in the Book He has giv-en, A
children a-way, He gathered them gently and bless'd them, And
read-y to bless. And so when His dear voice is call-ing, To

rit.

CHORUS.

welcome so wondrous we find.
still He is call-ing to-day, Children, chil-dren, come ye, O
Je-sus, O may we say "Yes."

rit.

come un-to me, Children, children, come ye, O come unto me.

Give Me Jesus

82

Arr. by M.

1. When I'm hap-py hear me sing, When I'm hap-py hear me sing,
2. When in sor-row hear me pray, When in sor-row hear me pray,
3. When in trou-ble hear me pray, When in trou-ble hear me pray,
4. When I'm lone-ly hear me sing, When I'm lone-ly hear me sing,
5. When I'm dy-ing hear me sing, When I'm dy-ing hear me sing,
6. When in glo-ry we will sing, When in glo-ry we will sing,

CHORUS.

When I'm hap-py hear me sing, Give me Je - sus. Give me Je - sus,
When in sor-row hear me pray, Give me Je - sus. Give me Je - sus,
When in trou-ble hear me pray, Give me Je - sus. Give me Je - sus,
When I'm lone-ly hear me sing, Give me Je - sus. Give me Je - sus,
When I'm dy-ing hear me sing, Give me Je - sus. Give me Je - sus,
When in glo-ry we will sing, Give me Je - sus. Give me Je - sus,

Give me Je - sus, You may have all the world, Give me Je - sus.

Copyright, 1905, by John A. Davis. Used by permission.

I Love Him

83

I love Him, I love Him, Be - cause He first loved me,

And pur - chased my sal - va - tion on Cal - v'ry's tree.

— 65 —

84   My Jesus, I Love Thee

London Hymn book, 1864   A. J. Gordon

1. My Je-sus, I love Thee, I know Thou art mine; For Thee all the
2. I love Thee because Thou hast first lov-ed me, And purchased my
3. I will love Thee in life, I will love Thee in death, And praise Thee as
4. In mansions of glo-ry and end-less de-light, I'll ev-er a-

fol-lies of sin I re-sign; My gra-cious Re-deem-er, my
par-don on Cal-va-ry's tree; I love Thee for wear-ing the
long as Thou lend-est me breath; And say when the death-dew lies
dore Thee in heav-en so bright; I'll sing with the glit-ter-ing

Sav-iour art Thou, If ev-er I loved Thee, my Je-sus, 'tis now.
thorns on Thy brow; If ev-er I loved Thee, my Je-sus, 'tis now.
cold on my brow, If ev-er I loved Thee, my Je-sus, 'tis now.
crown on my brow, If ev-er I loved Thee, my Je-sus, 'tis now.

85   Fairest Lord Jesus

Crusader's Hymn
4th stanza by Isabella H. Fiske   Arr. by Richard S. Willis

1. Fairest Lord Je-sus! Ru-ler of all na-ture! O Thou of God and man the Son!
2. Fair are the meadows, Fairer still the woodlands, Robed in the blooming garb of spring;
3. Fair is the sunshine, Fairer still the moonlight, And all the twinkling starry host;
4. Lord of the sunlight, Lord of the starlight, Lord of the seasons, teach me to know

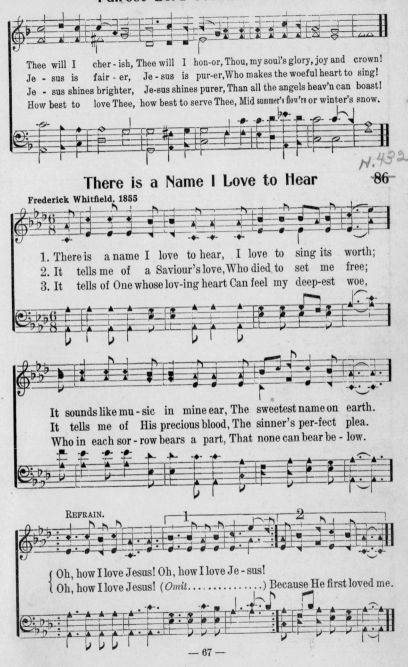

Thee will I   cher-ish, Thee will I hon-or, Thou, my soul's glory, joy and crown!
Je - sus is   fair-er,   Je - sus is pur-er, Who makes the woeful heart to sing!
Je - sus shines brighter, Je-sus shines purer, Than all the angels heav'n can boast!
How best to   love Thee, how best to serve Thee, Mid summer's flow'rs or winter's snow.

There is a Name I Love to Hear

86

H.432

Frederick Whitfield, 1855

1. There is   a name I love to hear, I love to   sing its   worth;
2. It   tells me of   a Saviour's love, Who died to   set me   free;
3. It   tells of One whose lov-ing heart Can feel my deep-est woe,

It sounds like mu - sic in mine ear, The sweetest name on earth.
It tells me of   His precious blood, The sinner's per-fect plea.
Who in each sor - row bears a part, That none can bear be - low.

REFRAIN.

{ Oh, how I love Jesus! Oh, how I love Je - sus!
{ Oh, how I love Jesus! (*Omit*..............) Because He first loved me.

87 # Love at Home

John H. McNaughton, 1829-1896
Tenderly.

John H. McNaughton
Arr. by J. D. Brunk, 1904

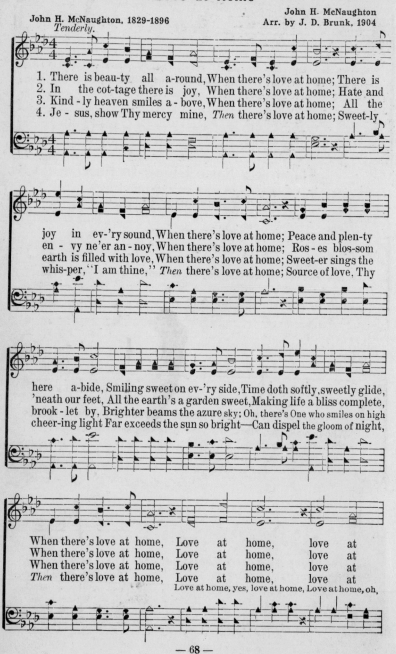

1. There is beau-ty all a-round, When there's love at home; There is
2. In the cot-tage there is joy, When there's love at home; Hate and
3. Kind-ly heaven smiles a-bove, When there's love at home; All the
4. Je-sus, show Thy mercy mine, *Then* there's love at home; Sweet-ly

joy in ev-'ry sound, When there's love at home; Peace and plen-ty
en-vy ne'er an-noy, When there's love at home; Ros-es blos-som
earth is filled with love, When there's love at home; Sweet-er sings the
whis-per, "I am thine," *Then* there's love at home; Source of love, Thy

here a-bide, Smiling sweet on ev-'ry side, Time doth softly, sweetly glide,
'neath our feet, All the earth's a garden sweet, Making life a bliss complete,
brook-let by, Brighter beams the azure sky; Oh, there's One who smiles on high
cheer-ing light Far exceeds the sun so bright—Can dispel the gloom of night,

When there's love at home, Love at home, love at
When there's love at home, Love at home, love at
When there's love at home, Love at home, love at
Then there's love at home, Love at home, love at
Love at home, yes, love at home, Love at home, oh,

Love at Home.—Concluded

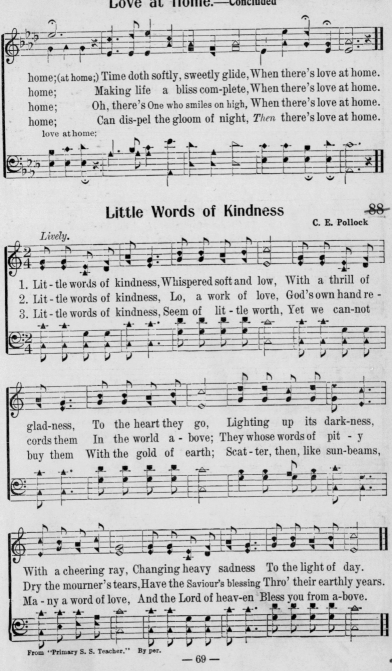

home;(at home;) Time doth softly, sweetly glide, When there's love at home.
home;   Making life a bliss com-plete, When there's love at home.
home;   Oh, there's One who smiles on high, When there's love at home.
home;   Can dis-pel the gloom of night, *Then* there's love at home.

love at home;

Little Words of Kindness

88

C. E. Pollock

Lively.

1. Lit - tle words of kindness, Whispered soft and low, With a thrill of
2. Lit - tle words of kindness, Lo, a work of love, God's own hand re -
3. Lit - tle words of kindness, Seem of lit - tle worth, Yet we can-not

glad-ness, To the heart they go, Lighting up its dark-ness,
cords them In the world a - bove; They whose words of pit - y
buy them With the gold of earth; Scat - ter, then, like sun-beams,

With a cheering ray, Changing heavy sadness To the light of day.
Dry the mourner's tears, Have the Saviour's blessing Thro' their earthly years.
Ma - ny a word of love, And the Lord of heav-en Bless you from a-bove.

From "Primary S. S. Teacher." By per.

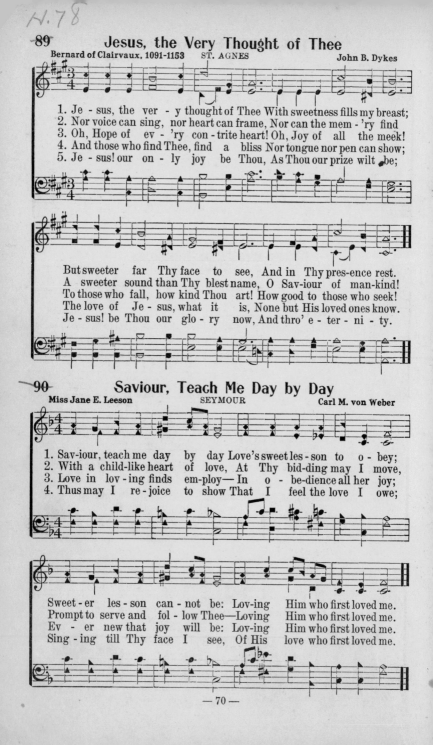

89 Jesus, the Very Thought of Thee

Bernard of Clairvaux, 1091-1153   ST. AGNES   John B. Dykes

1. Je - sus, the ver - y thought of Thee With sweetness fills my breast;
2. Nor voice can sing, nor heart can frame, Nor can the mem - 'ry find
3. Oh, Hope of ev - 'ry con - trite heart! Oh, Joy of all the meek!
4. And those who find Thee, find a bliss Nor tongue nor pen can show;
5. Je - sus! our on - ly joy be Thou, As Thou our prize wilt be;

But sweeter far Thy face to see, And in Thy pres-ence rest.
A sweeter sound than Thy blest name, O Sav-iour of man-kind!
To those who fall, how kind Thou art! How good to those who seek!
The love of Je - sus, what it is, None but His loved ones know.
Je - sus! be Thou our glo - ry now, And thro' e - ter - ni - ty.

90 Saviour, Teach Me Day by Day

Miss Jane E. Leeson   SEYMOUR   Carl M. von Weber

1. Sav-iour, teach me day by day Love's sweet les - son to o - bey;
2. With a child-like heart of love, At Thy bid-ding may I move,
3. Love in lov - ing finds em-ploy— In o - be-dience all her joy;
4. Thus may I re - joice to show That I feel the love I owe;

Sweet - er les - son can - not be: Lov-ing Him who first loved me.
Prompt to serve and fol - low Thee—Loving Him who first loved me.
Ev - er new that joy will be: Lov-ing Him who first loved me.
Sing - ing till Thy face I see, Of His love who first loved me.

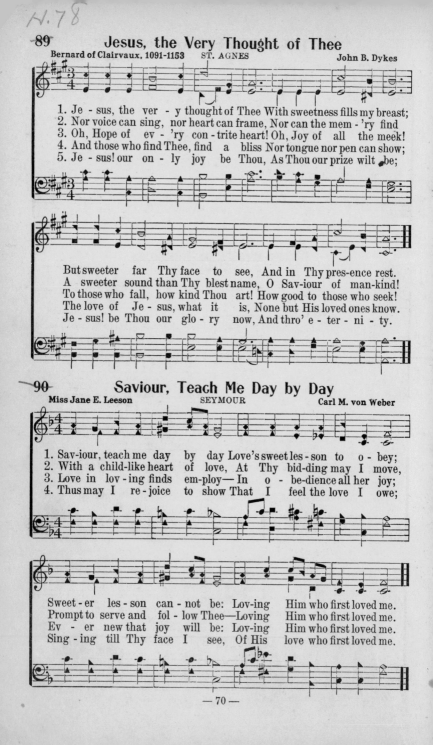

There is No Name So Sweet on Earth

George W. Bethune   THE BLESSED NAME   William B. Bradbury

1. There is no name so sweet on earth, No name so dear in heav-en,
2. 'Twas Gabriel first that did proclaim, To His most bless-ed moth-er,
3. And when He hung up-on the tree, They wrote His name a-bove Him,
4. So now up-on His Father's throne, Almighty to re-lieve us

As that be-fore His wondrous birth To Christ the Sav-iour giv-en.
That name which now and ev-er-more We praise a-bove all oth-er.
That all might see the rea-son we For ev-er-more must love Him.
From sin and pains, He ev-er reigns The Prince and Saviour, Je-sus.

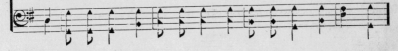

CHORUS.

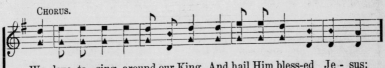

We love to sing around our King, And hail Him bless-ed Je-sus;

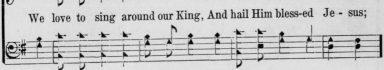

For there's no word ear ev-er heard So dear, so sweet as Je-sus.

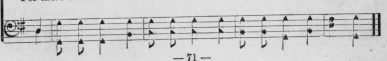

92 The Joy-Life

Lina Z. Ressler

Sylvia Borntrager

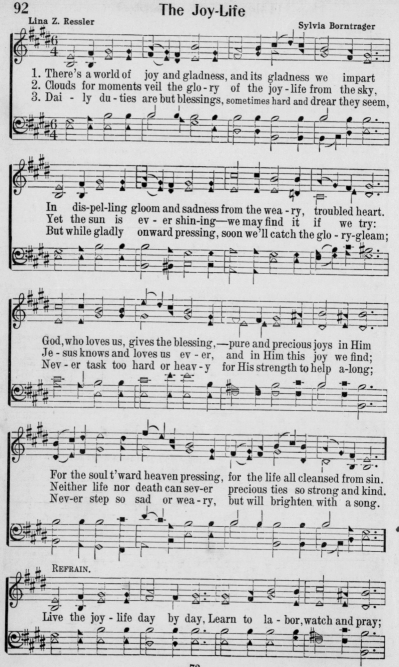

1. There's a world of joy and gladness, and its gladness we impart
2. Clouds for moments veil the glo-ry of the joy-life from the sky,
3. Dai-ly du-ties are but blessings, sometimes hard and drear they seem,

In dis-pel-ling gloom and sadness from the wea-ry, troubled heart.
Yet the sun is ev-er shin-ing—we may find it if we try:
But while gladly onward pressing, soon we'll catch the glo-ry-gleam;

God, who loves us, gives the blessing,—pure and precious joys in Him
Je-sus knows and loves us ev-er, and in Him this joy we find;
Nev-er task too hard or heav-y for His strength to help a-long;

For the soul t'ward heaven pressing, for the life all cleansed from sin.
Neither life nor death can sev-er precious ties so strong and kind.
Nev-er step so sad or wea-ry, but will brighten with a song.

REFRAIN.

Live the joy-life day by day, Learn to la-bor, watch and pray;

The Joy-Life.—Concluded

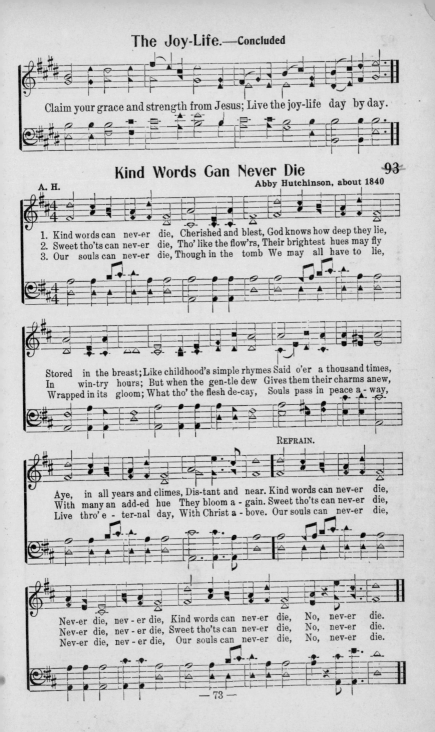

Claim your grace and strength from Jesus; Live the joy-life day by day.

Kind Words Can Never Die

93

A. H.

Abby Hutchinson, about 1840

1. Kind words can nev-er die, Cherished and blest, God knows how deep they lie,
2. Sweet tho'ts can nev-er die, Tho' like the flow'rs, Their brightest hues may fly
3. Our souls can nev-er die, Though in the tomb We may all have to lie,

Stored in the breast; Like childhood's simple rhymes Said o'er a thousand times,
In win-try hours; But when the gen-tle dew Gives them their charms anew,
Wrapped in its gloom; What tho' the flesh de-cay, Souls pass in peace a-way,

REFRAIN.

Aye, in all years and climes, Dis-tant and near. Kind words can nev-er die,
With many an add-ed hue They bloom a-gain. Sweet tho'ts can nev-er die,
Live thro' e-ter-nal day, With Christ a-bove. Our souls can nev-er die,

Nev-er die, nev-er die, Kind words can nev-er die, No, nev-er die.
Nev-er die, nev-er die, Sweet tho'ts can nev-er die, No, nev-er die.
Nev-er die, nev-er die, Our souls can nev-er die, No, nev-er die.

As a Shepherd

Robt. Morris, LL. D.

Chas. H. Gabriel, 1874

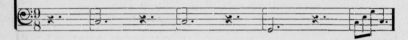

1. As   a shepherd He will lead them, To green pastures they shall go;
2. Near the well of   cooling wa - ter, In the sul - try noon of day,
3. If   up - on the   craggy mountain An-y lambs should flee a-way,

All   His blessings, as they need them, On the lambs He will be-stow.
Ev - 'ry lit - tle   son and daughter With the gentle   One shall stay.
Je - sus, from the   cooling fountain, Will o'ertake them where they stray,

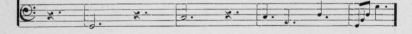

In   His bos-om,   when they languish, Precious children He will take,
Shepherd strong, He will defend them, Tho' the wolf be fierce and bold;
Will re-store each one, for - giv-en,   From the wild and ston-y waste,

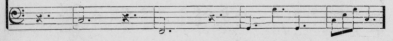

Where no blight, nor sin, nor anguish A - ny sor - row can a-wake.
Shepherd kind, He will attend them, Bring them safely to the fold.
And   within the   fold of heaven Bring the saved ones home at last.

As a Shepherd.—Concluded

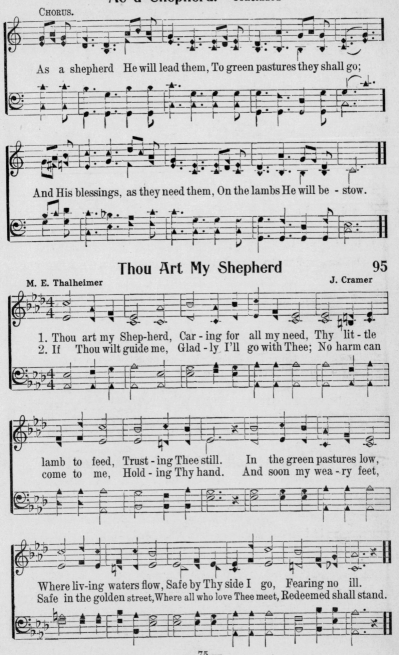

CHORUS.

As a shepherd He will lead them, To green pastures they shall go;

And His blessings, as they need them, On the lambs He will be - stow.

Thou Art My Shepherd

95

M. E. Thalheimer

J. Cramer

1. Thou art my Shep-herd, Car - ing for all my need, Thy lit - tle
2. If Thou wilt guide me, Glad - ly I'll go with Thee; No harm can

lamb to feed, Trust - ing Thee still. In the green pastures low,
come to me, Hold - ing Thy hand. And soon my wea - ry feet,

Where liv-ing waters flow, Safe by Thy side I go, Fearing no ill.
Safe in the golden street, Where all who love Thee meet, Redeemed shall stand.

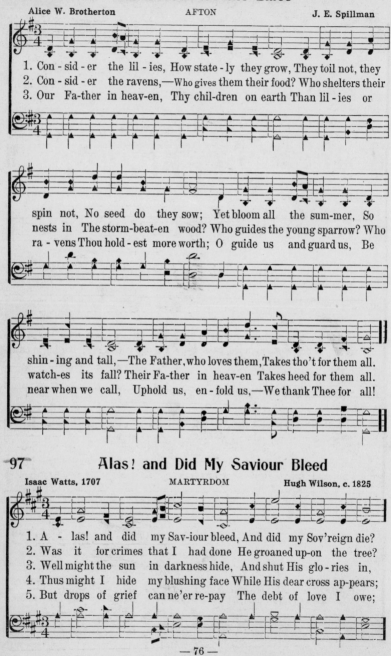

The Lesson Of the Lilies

Alice W. Brotherton   AFTON   J. E. Spillman

1. Con - sid - er   the lil - ies, How state - ly they grow, They toil not, they
2. Con - sid - er   the ravens,—Who gives them their food? Who shelters their
3. Our Fa - ther in heav - en, Thy chil-dren on earth Than lil - ies   or

spin not, No seed do they sow; Yet bloom all   the sum-mer, So
nests in The storm-beat-en wood? Who guides the young sparrow? Who
ra - vens Thou hold - est more worth; O guide us   and guard us, Be

shin - ing and tall,—The Father, who loves them, Takes tho't for them all.
watch-es its fall? Their Fa-ther in heav-en Takes heed for them all.
near when we call, Uphold us, en - fold us,—We thank Thee for all!

97   Alas! and Did My Saviour Bleed

Isaac Watts, 1707   MARTYRDOM   Hugh Wilson, c. 1825

1. A - las! and did   my Sav-iour bleed, And did my Sov'reign die?
2. Was it for crimes that I had done He groaned up-on the tree?
3. Well might the sun in darkness hide, And shut His glo - ries in,
4. Thus might I hide my blushing face While His dear cross ap-pears;
5. But drops of grief can ne'er re-pay The debt of love I owe;

Alas! and Did My Saviour Bleed.—Concluded

Would He de-vote that sa-cred head For such a worm as I?
A - maz-ing pit-y! Grace unknown! And love be-yond de-gree!
When God's own Son was cru-ci-fied For man the creature's sin.
Dis - solve my heart in thank-ful-ness, And melt mine eyes to tears.
Here, Lord, I give my-self a - way; 'Tis all that I can do.

Saviour, Like a Shepherd

98

Dorothy A. Thrupp

Wm. B. Bradbury

1. { Sav - iour, like a Shepherd lead us, Much we need Thy tend'rest care; }
   { In Thy pleasant pastures feed us; For our use Thy folds prepare. }

2. { We are Thine, do Thou be-friend us, Be the Guardian of our way; }
   { Keep Thy flock, from sin defend us, Seek us when we go a - stray. }

3. { Thou hast promised to re - ceive us, Poor and sin - ful tho' we be; }
   { Thou hast mer-cy to re - lieve us, Grace to cleanse and pow'r to free. }

Bless-ed Je - sus! blessed Je - sus! Thou hast bought us, Thine we are;
Bless-ed Je - sus! blessed Je - sus! Hear, O hear us, when we pray;
Bless-ed Je - sus! blessed Je - sus! We will ear - ly turn to Thee;

Blessed Je - sus! blessed Je-sus! Thou hast bought us Thine we are!
Blessed Je - sus! blessed Je-sus! Hear, O hear us, when we pray!
Blessed Je - sus! blessed Je-sus! We will ear - ly turn to Thee!

The Lord is My Shepherd

23rd Psalm   TYLER.   Arr. from Koschat by E. O. E.

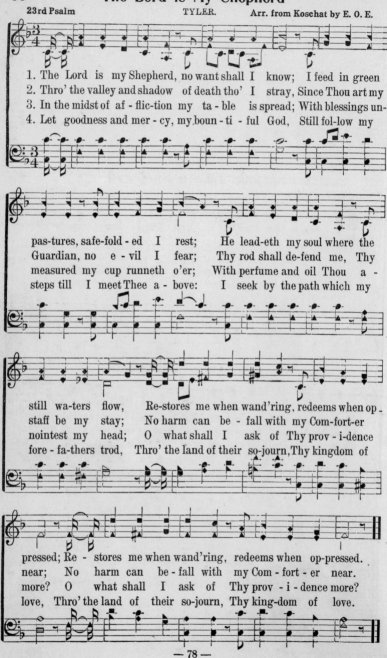

1. The Lord is my Shepherd, no want shall I know; I feed in green
pas-tures, safe-fold-ed I rest; He lead-eth my soul where the
still wa-ters flow, Re-stores me when wand'ring, redeems when op-
pressed; Re-stores me when wand'ring, redeems when op-pressed.

2. Thro' the valley and shadow of death tho' I stray, Since Thou art my
Guardian, no e-vil I fear; Thy rod shall de-fend me, Thy
staff be my stay; No harm can be-fall with my Com-fort-er
near; No harm can be-fall with my Com-fort-er near.

3. In the midst of af-flic-tion my ta-ble is spread; With blessings unmeasured my cup runneth o'er; With perfume and oil Thou a-
nointest my head; O what shall I ask of Thy prov-i-dence
more? O what shall I ask of Thy prov-i-dence more?

4. Let goodness and mer-cy, my boun-ti-ful God, Still fol-low my
steps till I meet Thee a-bove: I seek by the path which my
fore-fa-thers trod, Thro' the land of their so-journ, Thy kingdom of
love, Thro' the land of their so-journ, Thy king-dom of love.

Come to the Saviour

G. F. R.

Geo. F. Root

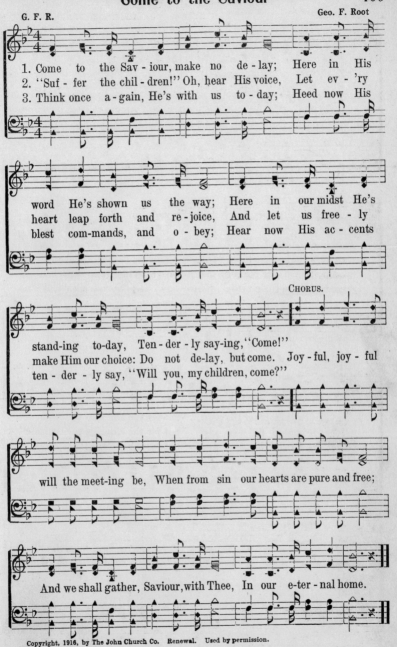

1. Come to the Sav - iour, make no de - lay; Here in His
2. "Suf - fer the chil - dren!" Oh, hear His voice, Let ev - 'ry
3. Think once a - gain, He's with us to - day; Heed now His

word He's shown us the way; Here in our midst He's
heart leap forth and re - joice, And let us free - ly
blest com-mands, and o - bey; Hear now His ac - cents

CHORUS.

stand-ing to-day, Ten - der - ly say-ing, "Come!"
make Him our choice: Do not de-lay, but come. Joy - ful, joy - ful
ten - der - ly say, "Will you, my children, come?"

will the meet-ing be, When from sin our hearts are pure and free;

And we shall gather, Saviour, with Thee, In our e - ter - nal home.

Suffer the Children to Come

Dr. I. L. Mitchell

W. A. Ogden

1. { Hark! I hear my Sav-iour say: "Suffer the children to come to me;"
   { Do not turn the lambs a-way, "Suffer the children to (*Omit* ......)

2. { Tell them Je-sus loves them all, "Suffer the children to come to me,"
   { He will guide them lest they fall, "Suffer the children to (*Omit* .....)

3. { Take them gently by the hand, "Suffer the children to come to me."
   { Lead them to the bet-ter land, "Suffer the children to (*Omit*......)

come." Point them to the Father's throne, Speak to them in tend'rest tone,
come." Oh, for-bid them not, I pray, Let the children come today,
come." Lead them with a will-ing mind, Tell them of a Saviour kind;

Je - sus calls them for His own, "Suf-fer the children to come."
Hear the blessed Sav-iour say: "Suf-fer the children to come."
They e - ter-nal life may find, "Suf-fer the children to come."

D. S.—*watch and pray,* "*Suf-fer the chil-dren to come.*"

FULL CHORUS,

Do not turn the lambs away, Precious in His sight are they, Teach them how to

Bring Them In

Alexcenah Thomas

W. A. Ogden

1. Hark! 'tis the Shepherd's voice I hear, Out in the des - ert
2. Who'll go and help this Shep-herd kind, Help Him the wand'ring
3. Out in the des - ert hear their cry; Out on the mountain

dark and drear, Call - ing the sheep who've gone astray, Far from the
ones to find? Who'll bring the lost ones to the fold, Where they'll be
wild and high, Hark! 'tis the Mas-ter speaks to thee, "Go, find my

CHORUS.

Shep-herd's fold a - way.
shel - tered from the cold? Bring them in, bring them in,
sheep, wher-e'er they be."

Bring them in from the fields of sin; Bring them in,

bring them in, Bring the wand'ring ones to Je - sus.

My Sins Were High as a Mountain

My sins were as high as a moun-tain, They all dis-ap-
peared in the fountain, He wrote my name down for a palace and crown,
And, praise His dear name, I am free, He free.

1 am free,

2 He free.

My Father's House

Arranged Chester K. Lehman

1. Ev - 'ry-thing's al - right in my Father's house, Ev-'ry-
2. There won't be an - y sin in my Father's house, There won't
3. I do want to go there, to my Father's house, I do
4. Don't you want to go there, to my Father's house, Don't you

thing's al - right in my Fa-ther's house, Ev - 'ry-thing's
be an - y sin in my Fa-ther's house, There won't be
want to go there, to my Fa-ther's house, I do want
want to go there, to my Fa-ther's house, Don't you want

al - right in my Father's house,
an - y sin in my Father's house,
to go there, to my Father's house,
to go there, to my Father's house? There is joy, joy, joy.

If I Come to Jesus

Fanny J. Crosby

W. H. Doane, 1867

1. If I come to Je-sus, He will make me glad; He will give me
2. If I come to Je-sus, He will hear my pray'r; He will love me
3. If I come to Je-sus, He will take my hand, He will kind-ly
4. There with happy children, Robed in snow-y white, I shall see my

REFRAIN.

pleas-ure, When my heart is sad.
dear-ly, He my sins did bear. If I come to Je-sus,
lead me To a bet-ter land.
Sav-iour In that world so bright.

Hap-py I shall be, He is gen-tly call-ing Lit-tle ones like me,

H.387

Rock of Ages

106

1

Rock of Ages, cleft for me,
Let me hide myself in Thee;
Let the water and the blood
From Thy riven side which flowed,
Be of sin the double cure,
Cleanse me from its guilt and pow'r.

2

Not the labor of my hands
Can fulfill the law's demands;
Could my zeal no respite know,
Could my tears forever flow,
All for sin could not atone,
Thou must save, and Thou alone.

3

Nothing in my hands I bring,
Simply to Thy cross I cling;
Naked, come to Thee for dress;
Helpless, look to Thee for grace;
Foul, I to the fountain fly;
Wash me, Saviour, or I die.

4

While I draw this fleeting breath,
When my heart-strings break in death,
When I soar to worlds unknown,
See Thee on Thy judgment throne,
Rock of Ages, cleft for me,
Let me hide myself in Thee.

A. M. Toplady

107   Can a Boy Forget His Mother?

J. H. W.   Prof. J. H. Weber.

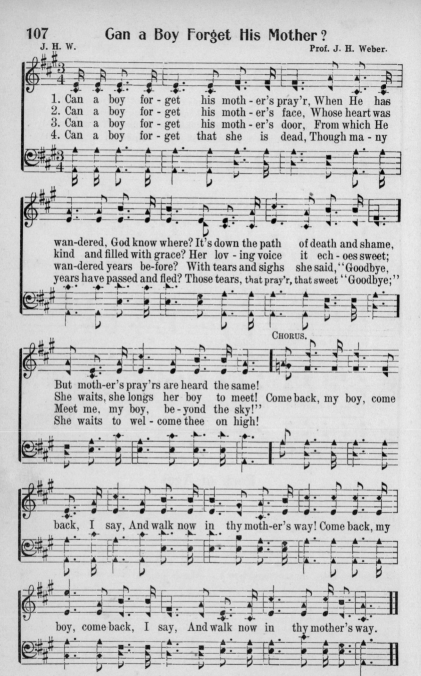

1. Can a boy for-get his moth-er's pray'r, When He has
2. Can a boy for-get his moth-er's face, Whose heart was
3. Can a boy for-get his moth-er's door, From which He
4. Can a boy for-get that she is dead, Though ma-ny

wan-dered, God know where? It's down the path   of death and shame,
kind and filled with grace? Her lov-ing voice   it ech-oes sweet;
wan-dered years be-fore? With tears and sighs   she said, "Goodbye,
years have passed and fled? Those tears, that pray'r, that sweet "Goodbye;"

CHORUS.

But moth-er's pray'rs are heard the same!
She waits, she longs her boy to meet! Come back, my boy, come
Meet me, my boy, be-yond the sky!"
She waits to wel-come thee on high!

back, I say, And walk now in thy moth-er's way! Come back, my

boy, come back, I say, And walk now in thy mother's way.

Footsteps Of Jesus

Mrs. M. B. C. Slade

Dr. A. B. Everett

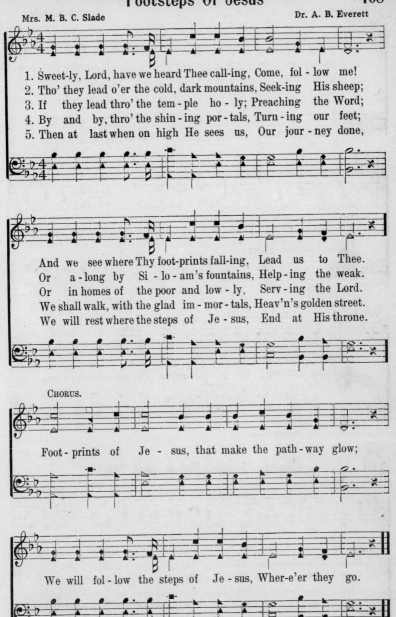

1. Sweet-ly, Lord, have we heard Thee call-ing, Come, fol - low me!
2. Tho' they lead o'er the cold, dark mountains, Seek-ing His sheep;
3. If they lead thro' the tem - ple ho - ly; Preaching the Word;
4. By and by, thro' the shin - ing por - tals, Turn - ing our feet;
5. Then at last when on high He sees us, Our jour - ney done,

And we see where Thy foot-prints fall-ing, Lead us to Thee.
Or a - long by Si - lo - am's fountains, Help - ing the weak.
Or in homes of the poor and low - ly, Serv - ing the Lord.
We shall walk, with the glad im - mor - tals, Heav'n's golden street.
We will rest where the steps of Je - sus, End at His throne.

CHORUS.

Foot - prints of Je - sus, that make the path - way glow;

We will fol - low the steps of Je - sus, Wher-e'er they go.

109   We are Little Pilgrims

Lizzie Ashbaugh

J. H. Kerzenknabe

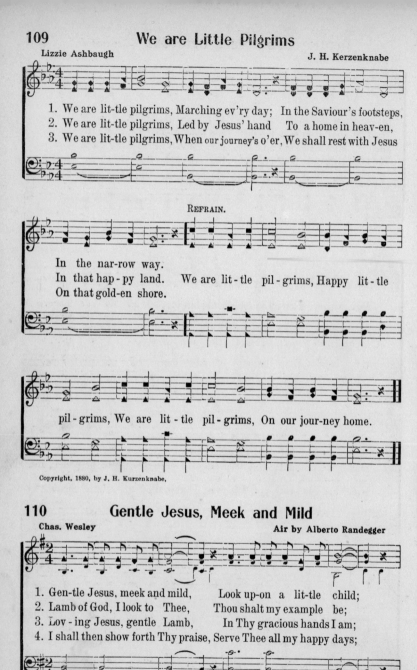

1. We are lit-tle pilgrims, Marching ev'ry day; In the Saviour's footsteps,
2. We are lit-tle pilgrims, Led by Jesus' hand To a home in heav-en,
3. We are lit-tle pilgrims, When our journey's o'er, We shall rest with Jesus

REFRAIN.

In the nar-row way.
In that hap-py land.   We are lit-tle pil-grims, Happy lit-tle
On that gold-en shore.

pil-grims, We are lit-tle pil-grims, On our jour-ney home.

Copyright, 1880, by J. H. Kurzenknabe,

110   Gentle Jesus, Meek and Mild

Chas. Wesley

Air by Alberto Randegger

1. Gen-tle Jesus, meek and mild,   Look up-on a lit-tle child;
2. Lamb of God, I look to Thee,   Thou shalt my example be;
3. Lov-ing Jesus, gentle Lamb,   In Thy gracious hands I am;
4. I shall then show forth Thy praise, Serve Thee all my happy days;

— 86 —

Gentle Jesus, Meek and Mild.—Concluded

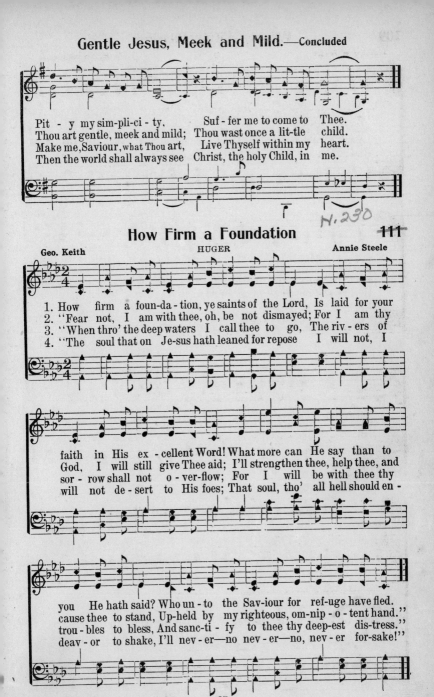

Pit - y my sim-pli-ci - ty, Suf - fer me to come to Thee.
Thou art gentle, meek and mild; Thou wast once a lit-tle child.
Make me, Saviour, what Thou art, Live Thyself within my heart.
Then the world shall always see Christ, the holy Child, in me.

How Firm a Foundation

111

Geo. Keith   HUGER   Annie Steele

1. How   firm a foun-da - tion, ye saints of the Lord, Is laid for your
2. "Fear not, I am with thee, oh, be not dismayed; For I   am thy
3. "When thro' the deep waters I call thee to go, The riv - ers of
4. "The   soul that on Je-sus hath leaned for repose   I will not, I

faith   in His ex - cellent Word! What more can He say   than to
God,   I will still give Thee aid; I'll strengthen thee, help thee, and
sor - row shall not o - ver-flow; For I will be with thee thy
will   not de - sert to His foes; That soul, tho' all hell should en -

you   He hath said? Who un - to the Sav-iour for ref-uge have fled.
cause thee to stand, Up-held by my righteous, om-nip - o - tent hand."
trou - bles to bless, And sanc-ti - fy to thee thy deep-est dis-tress."
deav - or to shake, I'll nev - er—no nev - er—no, nev - er for-sake!"

— 87 —

He Leadeth Me

112

Joseph H. Gilmore

William B. Bradbury

1. He lead-eth me: O bless-ed tho't! O words with heav'nly
2. Some-times 'mid scenes of deep-est gloom, Sometimes where E-den's
3. Lord, I would clasp Thy hand in mine, Nor ev-er mur-mur
4. And when my task on earth is done, When, by Thy grace, the

com-fort fraught! What-e'er I do, wher-e'er I be, Still
bow-ers bloom, By wa-ters calm—or troub-led sea,— Still
nor re-pine; Con-tent, what-ev-er lot I see, Since
vic-t'ry's won, E'en death's cold wave I will not flee, Since

REFRAIN.

'tis God's hand that lead-eth me.
'tis His hand that lead-eth me.   He lead-eth me, He
'tis my God that lead-eth me.
God thro' Jor-dan lead-eth me.

lead-eth me; By His own hand He lead-eth me: His

faith-ful fol-l'wer I would be, For by His hand He lead-eth me.

I Will Follow Thee

J. H. Rosecrans

1. Je - sus, I will fol - low Thee, For I hear Thee calling me;
2. Lit - tle eyes might lose the way, Lit - tle feet might go a - stray;
3. Grief and want may be my foes, Fool-ish sins my way op - pose;

Lov - ing, trust-ing, glad I come, To let Thee lead me home.
I might weak and wea - ry be, But Thou art strong for me.
Full of cour-age I will be, Whene'er I fol - low Thee.

CHORUS.

I will fol - low Thee, I will fol - low Thee,

I will fol - low Thee, Wher - ev - er Thou dost lead.

A Little Light

Mrs. W. B. D.   Mrs. W. B. Dingman

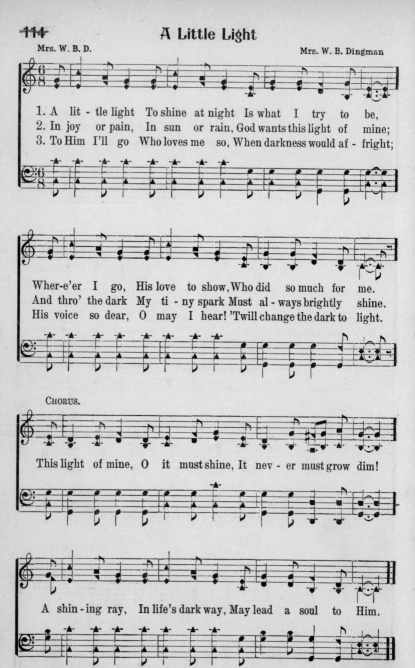

1. A lit - tle light To shine at night Is what I try to be,
2. In joy or pain, In sun or rain, God wants this light of mine;
3. To Him I'll go Who loves me so, When darkness would af - fright;

Wher-e'er I go, His love to show, Who did so much for me.
And thro' the dark My ti - ny spark Must al - ways brightly shine.
His voice so dear, O may I hear! 'Twill change the dark to light.

CHORUS.

This light of mine, O it must shine, It nev - er must grow dim!

A shin - ing ray, In life's dark way, May lead a soul to Him.

Near the Cross

Fanny J. Crosby

W. H. Doane, 1869

1. Je - sus, keep me near the cross, There a pre-cious foun - tain,
2. Near the cross, a trem-bling soul, Love and mer - cy found me,
3. Near the cross! O Lamb of God, Bring its scenes be - fore me,
4. Near the cross I'll watch and wait, Hop-ing, trust-ing ev - er,

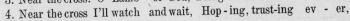

Free to all, a heal - ing stream, Flows from Calv'ry's moun-tain.
There the Bright and Morn-ing Star Shed His beams a - round me.
Help me walk from day to day, With its shad - ows o'er me.
Till I reach the gold - en strand, Just be-yond the riv - er.

REFRAIN.

In the cross, in the cross Be my glo - ry ev - er,

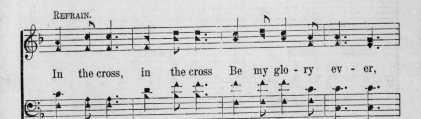

Till my rap-tured soul shall find Rest be-yond the riv - er.

Jesus Loves the Little Children

Rev. C. H. Woolston, D. D.

Geo. F. Root

1. Je - sus calls the children dear, "Come to me and nev - er fear,
2. Je - sus is the Shepherd true, And He'll al-ways stand by you,
3. I am com - ing, Lord, to Thee, And Thy sol - dier I will be,

For I love the lit - tle chil-dren of the world. I will take you
For He loves the lit - tle chil-dren of the world. He's a Sav-iour
For He loves the lit - tle chil-dren of the world. And His cross I'll

by the hand, Lead you to the bet - ter land, For I love the lit - tle
great and strong, And He'll shield you from the wrong, For He loves the lit - tle
al - ways bear, And for Him I'll do and dare, For He loves the lit - tle

CHORUS.

children of the world." Je-sus loves the lit - tle chil - dren, All the
lit - tle children, All the

children of the world; Red and yellow, black and white, They are
chil - dren of the world; brown,

— 92 —

Jesus Loves the Little Children.—Concluded

precious in His sight, Je-sus loves the lit - tle children of the world.

Jesus, Hear Thy Little Child

117

E. C. Greenlee

1. Sav-iour, bless a lit - tle child; Teach my heart the way to Thee;
2. I am young and Thou hast said, All who will may come to Thee;
3. Je - sus, help me, I am weak, Let me put my trust in Thee;
4. I would nev - er go a - stray, Nev - er turn a-side from Thee;

Make it gen - tle, good and mild, Lov-ing Sav-iour, care for me.
Feed my soul with liv - ing Bread, Lov-ing Sav-iour, care for me.
Teach me how and what to speak, Lov-ing Sav-iour, care for me.
Keep me in the heav'nly way, Lov-ing Sav-iour, care for me.

REFRAIN.

Sav - iour, lov - ing Sav - iour, Keep my feet al - way;

Lis - ten now, dear Sav - iour, Hear me when I pray.

118 Pity the Motherless

James Rowe

J. M. Henson

1. Oh, pit-y the dear lit-tle chil—dren, Whose fa-thers and
2. Speak kind-ly wher-ev-er you meet them, And show them that
2. Your love and your help they are need-ing, To help them to

moth-ers have gone; Their path thro' the world try to bright-en, And
you are a friend; Have words of en-cour-age-ment read-y, And
stand in the strife, And be for the heav-en-ly Fa-ther, True

Chorus.

sweet-ly en-cour-age them on. . . . .
oth-er good blessings to lend. . . . Oh, pit-y the moth-er-less,
ser-vants and blessings thro' life. . . . .

fatherless ones, And show them true kindness and love; For what you im-

part to each sad or-phan heart, The Lord will re-ward you a-bove.

J. M. Henson, owner. Used by permission.

To Send Across the Sea

E. E. Hewitt

F. H. H. Thomson

1. This mon - ey is for Je - sus; Some hap - py work to do
2. This mon - ey is for Je - sus; To send a - cross the sea
3. This mon - ey is for Je - sus; His fa - vor He will show;

For some of His dear chil-dren, Some serv - ice sweet and true.
The hap - py, hap - py ti - dings So dear to you and me.
We pray that He will bless it Wher - ev - er it may go.

CHORUS.

'Tis love that we are bring-ing, What-ev - er else we bring;

'Tis love that keeps us sing - ing To Christ our heav'n-ly King.

From "Primary Songs No. 2." Used by permission.

120 Little Children Far Away

Elizabeth Wood

Maurice A. Clifton

1. Lit - tle chil-dren far a - way, Lov-ing gifts we bring to - day;
2. Lit - tle chil-dren far a - way, Je - sus calls, His Word o - bey;
3. Lit - tle chil-dren far a - way, For you we will work and pray;

That of Je - sus you may learn, And to Christ the Saviour turn.
Hear and heed His lov - ing call, For He loves the children all.
And our gifts we'll glad-ly send, Tell-ing you of Christ our friend.

CHORUS.

Lit - tle chil-dren far a - way, Lov-ing gifts we're bring - ing;

That you too may know our Friend, And His praise be sing - ing.

121 H.409 Take My Life, and Let It Be

Frances R. Havergal, 1874

ELLINGHAM

S. N. Godfrey, 1881

1. Take my life, and let it be Con - se-crat - ed, Lord, to Thee:
2. Take my feet, and let them be Swift and beau-ti - ful for Thee;
3. Take my sil - ver and my gold; Not a mite would I with-hold;
4. Take my will and make it Thine, It shall be no long - er mine;
5. Take my love; my Lord, I pour At Thy feet its treas-ure-store;

Take My Life, and Let It Be.—Concluded

Take my moments and my days,
Let them flow in cease - less praise.

Take my voice, and let me sing
Al-ways, on - ly for my King.

Take my moments and my days,
Let them flow in cease - less praise.

Take my heart, it is Thine own,
It shall be Thy roy - al throne.

Take my-self and I will be
Ev - er, on - ly, all for Thee.

One Little Star 122

Susan Coolidge
Allegretto.
Gascon Carol

1. One lit - tle star in the star - ry night, One lit - tle
2. One lit - tle flow'r in the flow-er - ful spring, One lit - tle
3. Each lit - tle star has its spec - ial ray, Each lit - tle
4. Each lit - tle child can some love - work find, Each lit - tle

beam in the noon - day light, One lit - tle drop in the
feath - er in one lit - tle wing, One lit - tle note when the
beam has its place in the day, Each lit - tle riv - er drop
hand and each lit - tle mind, All can be gen - tle and

riv - er's might, What can they do, oh, what can they do?
man - y birds sing, All are so lit - tle, fee-ble and few.
im-pulse and sway; Feath-er and flow - er and songlet help too.
use - ful and kind, Though they are lit - tle, like me and like you.

— 97 —

123 We Are But a Band of Children

Mary Irene McLean
Not too fast.

Matt. 28: 19

A. F. Myers

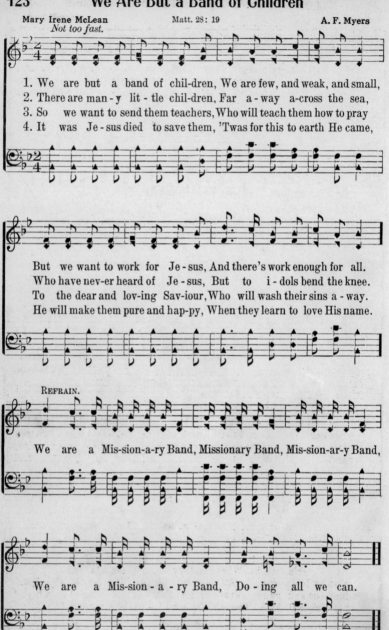

1. We are but a band of chil-dren, We are few, and weak, and small,
2. There are man-y lit-tle chil-dren, Far a-way a-cross the sea,
3. So we want to send them teachers, Who will teach them how to pray
4. It was Je-sus died to save them, 'Twas for this to earth He came,

But we want to work for Je-sus, And there's work enough for all.
Who have nev-er heard of Je-sus, But to i-dols bend the knee.
To the dear and lov-ing Sav-iour, Who will wash their sins a-way.
He will make them pure and hap-py, When they learn to love His name.

REFRAIN.

We are a Mis-sion-a-ry Band, Missionary Band, Mis-sion-ar-y Band,

We are a Mis-sion-a-ry Band, Do-ing all we can.

Yield Not to Temptation

H. R. Palmer   H. R. Palmer

1. Yield not to temp-ta-tion, For yielding is sin; Each vict'ry will
2. Shun e - vil companions, Bad language dis - dain, God's name hold in
3. To him that o'ercometh God giv-eth a crown; Thro' faith we shall

help you Some oth - er to win; Fight man-ful - ly on - ward,
rev'rence Nor take it in vain; Be thoughtful and earn - est,
con - quer, Tho' oft-en cast down; He who is our Sav - iour,

Dark passions sub-due, Look ev-er to Je-sus, He'll car-ry you through.
Kind-hearted and true, Look ev-er to Je-sus, He'll car-ry you through.
Our strength will renew, Look ev-er to Je-sus. He'll car-ry you through.

CHORUS.

Ask the Sav-iour to help you, Comfort, strengthen and keep you;

He is will-ing to aid you, He will car - ry you through.

125 The Star of Bethlehem

Levi Mumaw

Chas. H. Gabriel

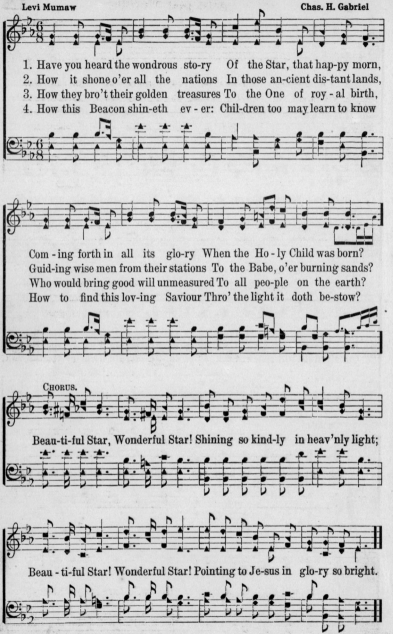

1. Have you heard the wondrous sto-ry   Of the Star, that hap-py morn,
2. How it shone o'er all the nations In those an-cient dis-tant lands,
3. How they bro't their golden treasures To the One of roy-al birth,
4. How this Beacon shin-eth ev - er: Chil-dren too may learn to know

Com - ing forth in all its glo-ry When the Ho - ly Child was born?
Guid-ing wise men from their stations To the Babe, o'er burning sands?
Who would bring good will unmeasured To all peo-ple on the earth?
How to find this lov-ing Saviour Thro' the light it doth be-stow?

CHORUS.

Beau-ti-ful Star, Wonderful Star! Shining so kind-ly in heav'nly light;

Beau - ti-ful Star! Wonderful Star! Pointing to Je-sus in glo-ry so bright.

On a Christmas Morning

Old Melody

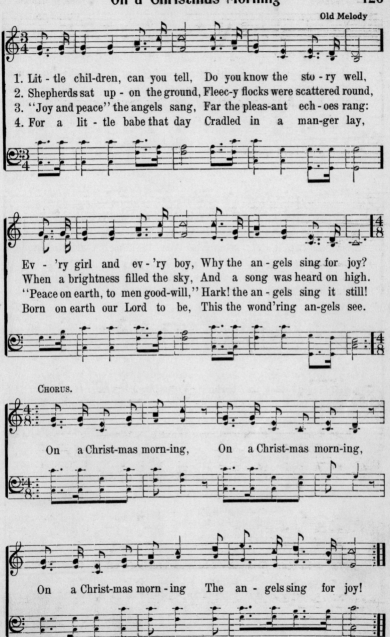

1. Lit - tle chil-dren, can you tell, Do you know the sto - ry well,
2. Shepherds sat up - on the ground, Fleec-y flocks were scattered round,
3. "Joy and peace" the angels sang, Far the pleas-ant ech - oes rang:
4. For a lit - tle babe that day Cradled in a man-ger lay,

Ev - 'ry girl and ev - 'ry boy, Why the an - gels sing for joy?
When a brightness filled the sky, And a song was heard on high.
"Peace on earth, to men good-will," Hark! the an - gels sing it still!
Born on earth our Lord to be, This the wond'ring an-gels see.

CHORUS.

On a Christ-mas morn-ing, On a Christ-mas morn-ing,

On a Christ-mas morn - ing The an - gels sing for joy!

127 ## Silent Night

Joseph Mohr, 1818

Franz Gruber

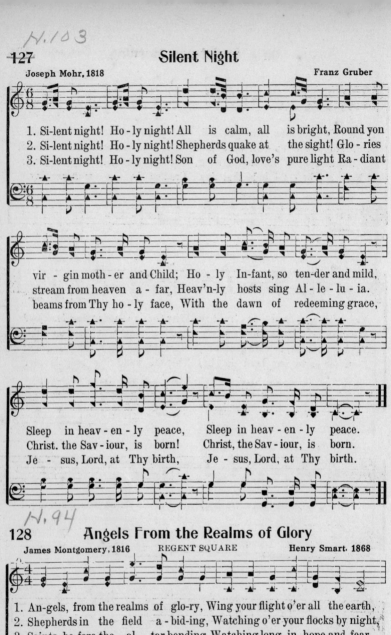

1. Si-lent night! Ho-ly night! All   is calm, all   is bright, Round yon
2. Si-lent night! Ho-ly night! Shepherds quake at   the sight! Glo-ries
3. Si-lent night! Ho-ly night! Son   of   God, love's   pure light Ra-diant

vir - gin moth - er and Child; Ho - ly   In-fant, so ten-der and mild,
stream from heaven a - far, Heav'n-ly   hosts sing Al - le - lu - ia.
beams from Thy ho - ly face, With the   dawn of   redeeming grace,

Sleep   in heav - en - ly   peace,   Sleep in heav - en - ly   peace.
Christ. the Sav - iour, is   born!   Christ, the Sav - iour, is   born.
Je - sus, Lord, at Thy birth,   Je - sus, Lord, at Thy   birth.

128 ## Angels From the Realms of Glory

James Montgomery, 1816

REGENT SQUARE

Henry Smart. 1868

1. An-gels, from the realms of glo-ry, Wing your flight o'er all the earth,
2. Shepherds in the field a - bid-ing, Watching o'er your flocks by night,
3. Saints, be-fore the al - tar bending, Watching long in hope and fear,
4. Sinners, wrung with true repentance, Doomed for guilt to end-less pains,

Angels From the Realms of Glory.—Concluded

Ye who sang cre - a - tion's sto - ry, Now proclaim Mes-si - ah's birth:
God with man is now re - sid - ing, Yon-der shines the in - fant light:
Sud - den-ly the Lord de-scend-ing, In His tem - ple shall ap - pear:
Jus-tice now revokes the sentence, Mer-cy calls you, break your chains:

Come and worship, Come and worship, Worship Christ, the new born King.

Joy to the World

ANTIOCH

Isaac Watts, 1719   Arr. by Lowell Mason, 1830

129

1. Joy to the world! the Lord is come! Let earth re-ceive her King;
2. Joy to the earth! the Saviour reigns! Let men their songs em-ploy;
3. He rules the world with truth and grace; And makes the nations prove

Let ev - 'ry heart pre-pare Him room, And heav'n and nature sing,
While fields and floods, rocks, hills and plains, Repeat the sounding joy,
The glo-ries of His righteousness, And wonders of His love,
And heav'n and na-

And heav'n and nature sing, And heav'n, and heav'n and na-ture sing.
Re-peat the sounding joy, Re - peat, re - peat the sounding joy.
And wonders of His love, And won-ders, won-ders of His love.
ture sing, And heav'n and nature sing. And heav'n and na-ture sing.

130 Luther's Cradle Hymn

Words and music by Martin Luther

1. A - way in a man - ger, No crib for His bed, The lit - tle Lord
2. The cat - tle are low - ing, The poor ba - by wakes, But lit - tle Lord
3. Be near me, Lord Je - sus; I ask Thee to stay Close by me for -

Je - sus Laid down His sweet head; The stars in the sky Looked
Je - sus, No cry - ing He makes. I love Thee, Lord Je - sus! Look
ev - er, And love me, I pray. Bless all the dear children In

down where He lay,—The lit - tle Lord Je - sus, A - sleep on the hay.
down from the sky, And stay by my crib - side, Watch my lul - la - by.
Thy ten - der care, And fit us for heav - en, To live with Thee there.

131 The Christmas Manger Hymn

Martin Luther

J. E. Spilman

1. A - way in a man - ger, No crib for His bed, The lit - tle Lord
2. The cat - tle are low - ing, The poor ba - by wakes, But lit - tle Lord
3. Be near me, Lord Je - sus; I ask Thee to stay Close by me for -

Je - sus Laid down His sweet head; The stars in the sky they Looked
Je - sus, No cry - ing He makes. I love Thee, Lord, Je - sus, Look
ev - er, And love me, I pray. Bless all the dear chil - dren In

The Christmas Manger Hymn.—Concluded

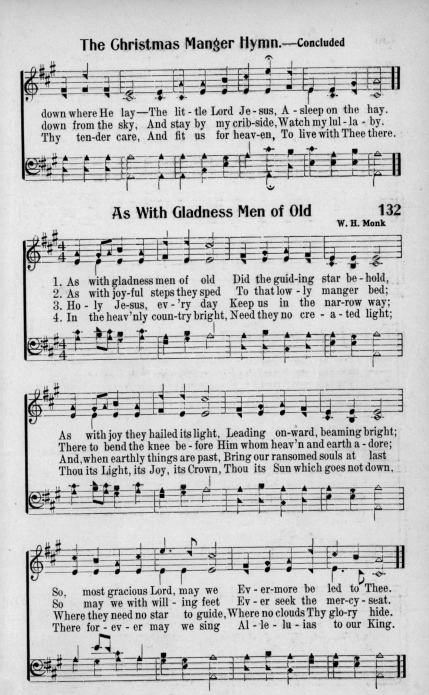

down where He lay—The lit - tle Lord Je - sus, A - sleep on the hay.
down from the sky, And stay by my crib-side, Watch my lul - la - by.
Thy ten-der care, And fit us for heav-en, To live with Thee there.

As With Gladness Men of Old
132
W. H. Monk

1. As with gladness men of old Did the guid-ing star be - hold,
2. As with joy-ful steps they sped To that low - ly manger bed;
3. Ho - ly Je-sus, ev - 'ry day Keep us in the nar-row way;
4. In the heav'nly coun-try bright, Need they no cre - a - ted light;

As with joy they hailed its light, Leading on-ward, beaming bright;
There to bend the knee be - fore Him whom heav'n and earth a - dore;
And, when earthly things are past, Bring our ransomed souls at last
Thou its Light, its Joy, its Crown, Thou its Sun which goes not down,

So, most gracious Lord, may we Ev - er-more be led to Thee.
So may we with will - ing feet Ev - er seek the mer-cy - seat.
Where they need no star to guide, Where no clouds Thy glo-ry hide.
There for - ev - er may we sing Al - le - lu - ias to our King.

O Come, All Ye Faithful

From Lat. F. Oakley, 1802-1880
William Mercer, v. 2

ADESTE FIDELES

J. Reading
Ward's Cantus Diversa, 1751

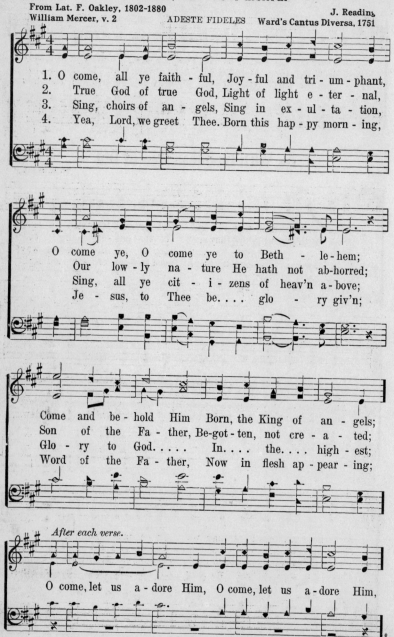

1. O come, all ye faith - ful, Joy - ful and tri - um - phant,
2. True God of true God, Light of light e - ter - nal,
3. Sing, choirs of an - gels, Sing in ex - ul - ta - tion,
4. Yea, Lord, we greet Thee. Born this hap - py morn - ing:

O come ye, O come ye to Beth - le - hem;
Our low - ly na - ture He hath not ab-horred;
Sing, all ye cit - i - zens of heav'n a - bove;
Je - sus, to Thee be.... glo - ry giv'n;

Come and be - hold Him Born, the King of an - gels;
Son of the Fa - ther, Be-got - ten, not cre - a - ted;
Glo - ry to God..... In.... the.... high - est;
Word of the Fa - ther, Now in flesh ap - pear - ing;

After each verse.

O come, let us a - dore Him, O come, let us a - dore Him,

O Come, All Ye Faithful.—Concluded

O come, let us a-dore Him, Christ, the Lord.

Jesus, the Light of the World 134

G. D. E.

G. D. Elderkin, arr.

1. Hark! the Her - ald an - gels sing, Je-sus, the Light of the world;
2. Joy - ful, all ye na - tions rise. Je-sus, the Light of the world;
2. Christ, by high - est heav'n a - dored, Je-sus, the Light of the world;
4. Hail the heav'n-born Prince of Peace, Je-sus, the Light of the world;

Glo - ry to the new-born King, Je-sus, the Light of the world.
Join the tri-umphs of the skies, Je-sus, the Light of the world.
Christ, the ev - er - last - ing Lord, Je-sus, the Light of the world.
Hail the Son of right-eous-ness, Je-sus, the Light of the world.

CHORUS.

We'll walk in the light, beautiful light, Come where the dewdrops of mercy are bright,

Shine all around us by day and by night, Jesus, the Light of the world.

135 O Little Town of Bethlehem

Phillips Brooks, 1868   ST. LOUIS   L. H. Redner

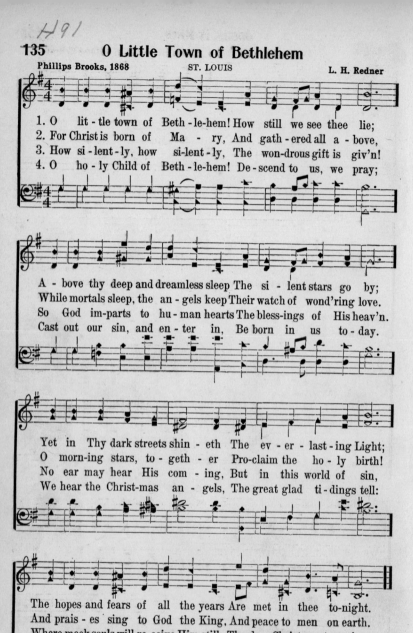

1. O lit-tle town of Beth-le-hem! How still we see thee lie;
2. For Christ is born of Ma - ry, And gath-ered all a-bove,
3. How si-lent-ly, how si-lent-ly, The won-drous gift is giv'n!
4. O ho - ly Child of Beth-le-hem! De-scend to us, we pray;

A - bove thy deep and dreamless sleep The si - lent stars go by;
While mortals sleep, the an - gels keep Their watch of wond'ring love.
So God im-parts to hu - man hearts The bless-ings of His heav'n.
Cast out our sin, and en - ter in, Be born in us to - day.

Yet in Thy dark streets shin - eth The ev - er - last-ing Light;
O morn-ing stars, to - geth - er Pro-claim the ho - ly birth!
No ear may hear His com - ing, But in this world of sin,
We hear the Christ-mas an - gels, The great glad ti - dings tell:

The hopes and fears of all the years Are met in thee to-night.
And prais - es sing to God the King, And peace to men on earth.
Where meek souls will re-ceive Him still, The dear Christ en - ters in.
O come to us, a - bide with us, Our Lord Em-man - u - el!

Jesus is King

L. Z. R.

Lina Z. Ressler

1. Tell the glad sto - ry that Je - sus is King; Tell it with joy,
2. Chil-dren in glad-ness this mes-sage may hear, Je - sus is King,
3. Hon - or His pres-ence by serv-ing Him well— Je - sus is King,

tell it a - gain. Teach all the na-tions His prais-es to sing,—
Je - sus is King; Peo - ple in lov - ing o - be-dience draw near,
Je - sus is King. Lov - ing - ly serve and His ten-der-ness tell—

REFRAIN.

Tell the glad sto - ry a - gain.
Je - sus to hon - or as King. Tell the sweet mes-sage a -
Je - sus we hon - or as King.

gain and a - gain, Je - sus doth love and doth save fall - en men.

Bear the news onward, ye heralds so brave, Je-sus is mighty to save.

Breaks the Joyful Easter Dawn

Lucy Larcom

1. Breaks the joy - ful Eas - ter dawn, Clear-er yet and strong-er;
2. Roused by Him from drear - y hours, Un - der snow-drifts chill - y,—
3. O - pen, hap - py hours of Spring, For the sun has ris - en;

Win-ter from the world has gone, Death shall be no lon - ger.
In His hands He brings the flow'rs, Brings the rose and lil - y.
Thro' the sky glad voic - es ring, Call - ing you from pris - on.

Far a - way good an-gels drive Night and sin and sad - ness;
Ev - 'ry lit - tle bur -ied bud In - to life He rais - es;
Lit - tle chil-dren dear, look up, T'ward His brightness press - ing,

Earth a-wakes in smiles, a - live With her dear Lord's glad-ness.
Ev - 'ry wild-flow'r of the wood Chants the dear Lord's prais - es.
Lift up, ev - 'ry heart, a cup For the dear Lord's bless - ing.

REFRAIN.

Breaks the joy - ful Eas - ter dawn, Clear - er yet and strong - er;

Breaks the Joyful Easter Dawn—Concluded

Win - ter from the world has gone, Death shall be no lon - ger.

The Promised Land

138

1. I have a Fa-ther in the promised land, I have a Fa-ther in the
2. I have a Sav-iour in the promised land, I have a Saviour in the
3. I have a crown in the promised land, I have a crown in the
4. I hope to meet you in the promised land, I hope to meet you in the

FINE.

prom-ised land; My Fa - ther calls me, I must go, To meet Him in the promised land.
prom-ised land; My Sav - iour calls me, I must go, To meet Him in the promised land.
prom-ised land; When Je-sus calls me, I must go, To wear it in the promised land.
prom-ised land; At Je - sus' feet, a joyous band, We'll praise Him in the promised land.

CHORUS.

D. S.

I'll a-way, I'll a-way to the prom-ised land; I'll a-way, I'll a-way to the
I'll a-way, I'll a-way to the prom-ised land; I'll a-way, I'll a-way to the
I'll a-way, I'll a-way to the prom-ised land; I'll a-way, I'll a-way to the
I'll a-way, I'll a-way to the prom-ised land; I'll a-way, I'll a-way to the

Christ is Risen

Soprano and Alto Duet

Chauncey J. King

1. Earth is bright, the lil-ies sing, Christ is ris-en, Christ our King!
2. Birds are warbling on the wing, Christ is ris-en, Christ our King!
3. Sunbeams bright, the good news bring, Christ is ris-en, Christ our King!

In their sweetness hear them say, Je-sus Christ is ris-en to-day.
Peeping, twittering, hear them say, Je-sus Christ is ris-en to-day.
Hark! and hear their joy-ful lay, Je-sus Christ is ris-en to-day.

CHORUS.

Joy-ful-ly the children sing, Christ is ris-en, Christ our King!

Hear them car-ol on their way, Je-sus Christ is ris-en to-day.

Shall We Gather at the River

Robert Lowry, 1864　　　　　　　　　　　　　　　Robert Lowry

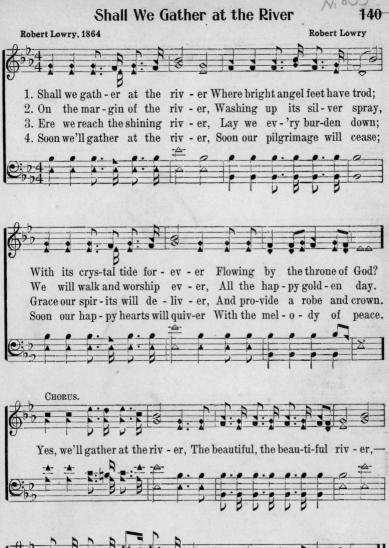

1. Shall we gath-er at the riv-er Where bright angel feet have trod;
2. On the mar-gin of the riv-er, Washing up its sil-ver spray,
3. Ere we reach the shining riv-er, Lay we ev-'ry bur-den down;
4. Soon we'll gather at the riv-er, Soon our pilgrimage will cease;

With its crys-tal tide for-ev-er Flowing by the throne of God?
We will walk and worship ev-er, All the hap-py gold-en day.
Grace our spir-its will de-liv-er, And pro-vide a robe and crown.
Soon our hap-py hearts will quiv-er With the mel-o-dy of peace.

CHORUS.

Yes, we'll gather at the riv-er, The beautiful, the beau-ti-ful riv-er,—

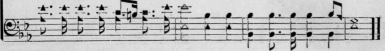

Gath-er with the saints at the riv-er, That flows by the throne of God.

I Shall Be Like Him

W. A. S.

W. A. Spencer

1. When I shall reach the more ex-cel-lent glo-ry, And all my
2. We shall not wait till the glo-ri-ous dawning Breaks on the
3. More and more like Him, re-peat the blest sto-ry, O-ver and

tri-als are passed, I shall be-hold Him, O won-der-ful sto-ry!
vis-ion so fair, Now we may welcome the heav-en-ly morn-ing,
o-ver a-gain, Changed by His spir-it from glo-ry to glo-ry,

CHORUS.

I shall be like Him at last.
Now we His im-age may bear. I shall be like Him, I shall be
I shall be sat-is-fied then.

like Him, And in His beau-ty shall shine, I shall be like Him,

I Shall Be Like Him.—Concluded

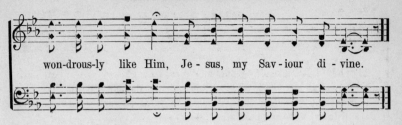

won-drous-ly like Him, Je-sus, my Sav-iour di-vine.

There is a Happy Land   142

Andrew Young, 1843   HAPPY LAND   Indian Air

1. There is a hap-py land, Far, far away, Where saints in glory stand,
2. Come to that hap-py land, Come, come away; Why will ye doubting stand,
3. Bright in that hap-py land, Beams ev'ry eye; Kept by a Father's hand,

Bright, bright as day. O how they sweet-ly sing, "Wor-thy is our
Why still de-lay? O we shall hap-py be, When from sin and
Love can-not die. O then to glo-ry run; Be a crown and

Sav-iour King," Loud let His prais-es ring, Praise, praise for aye!
sor-row free, Lord, we shall dwell with Thee, Blest, blest for aye!
Kingdom won, And bright, a-bove the sun, We'll reign for aye!

JESUS, KEEP ME NEAR THE CROSS

1. Gen - e - sis and Ex - o - dus, Levit - i - cus and Num - bers;
2. Es - ther, Job, and then the Psalms, Proverbs, Ec-cle - si - as - tes;
3. Mat-thew, Mark and Luke and John, Acts of the A - pos - tles,

Deu - ter - on - o - my the next, Josh - ua, Judg - es, Ruth.
Song of Sol - o - mon comes next, Fol-lowed by I - sa - iah,
Ro - mans, two Co - rin - thi - ans, Gala-tians and E - phe - sians.

First and Second Sam - u - el, First and Sec - ond Kings;
Jer - e - miah, Lam - en-tations, Eze - ki - el and Dan - iel;
D.S.—Jo - nah, Mi - cah, Na - hum and Ha - bak - kuk,
Philip-pi-ans, Colos - si - ans, And two Thes - sa - lo - nians;
D.S.—He - brews, next is James, First and Sec - ond Pe - ter,

FINE.

First and Sec - ond Chron - i - cles, Ez - ra, Ne - he - mi - ah.
Ho - se - a, and Jo - el next, A - mos, O - ba - di - ah.—*D.S.*
Zeph - a - ni - ah, Hag - ga - i, Zech - a - ri - ah, Mala - chi.
First and Sec - ond Tim - o - thy, Ti - tus and Phi - le - mon.—*D.S.*
First and Sec - ond and Third John, Jude, and Rev - e - la - tion.

Gloria Patri 144

Charles Meineke

Glo - ry be to the Fa-ther, and to the Son, and to the Ho - ly Ghost; As it
was in the beginning, is now, and ever shall be, world without end. Amen, A-men.

The Lord's Prayer 145

1. Our Father who art in heaven, hallowed be Thy name,
2. Give us this day our dai - ly bread,
3. And lead us not into temptation, but deliver us from evil,

Thy kingdom come, Thy will be done on earth as it is in heav'n.
And forgive us our trespasses, as we forgive them that trespass a - gainst us.
For Thine is the kingdom, and the power, and the glory, for - ever, A - men.

Old Hundred 146

Guillaume Franc, 1543

Praise God from Whom all bless-ings flow, Praise Him all crea-tures here be - low;
Praise Him a - bove ye heav'n-ly host; Praise Fa-ther, Son, and Ho - ly Ghost.

H 28

~~147~~ Holy, Holy, Holy

Key of E

Holy, holy, holy, Lord God Almighty!
Early in the morning our songs shall rise to Thee;
Holy, holy, holy, Merciful, and mighty,
God in three persons, blessed Trinity!

Holy, holy, holy, all the saints adore Thee,
Casting down their golden crowns around the glassy sea;
Cherubim and seraphim falling down before Thee,
Which wert, and art, and evermore shalt be.

Holy, holy, holy, though the darkness hide Thee,
Tho' the eye of sinful man Thy glory may not see;
Only Thou art Holy! there is none beside Thee,
Perfect in pow'r, in love, in purity.

Holy, holy, holy, Lord God Almighty!
All Thy works shall praise Thy name in earth, and sky, and sea;
Holy, holy, holy, merciful and mighty,
God in three persons, blessed Trinity!

~~148~~ H 389 My Faith Looks Up to Thee

Key of E.

My faith looks up to Thee,
Thou Lamb of Calvary,
Savior divine!
Now hear me while I pray,
Take all my guilt away,
Oh, let me from this day
Be wholly Thine.

May Thy rich grace impart
Strength to my fainting heart,
My zeal inspire;
As Thou hast died for me,
Oh, may my love to Thee
Pure, warm, and changeless be,
A living fire.

While life's dark maze I tread,
And griefs around me spread,
Be Thou my guide;
Bid darkness turn to day,
Wipe sorrow's tears away,
Nor let me ever stray
From Thee aside.

When ends life's transient dream,
When death's cold, sullen stream
Shall o'er me roll,
Blest Saviour, then, in love,
Fear and distrust remove;
Oh, bear me safe above,
A ransomed soul!

~~149~~ H. 375 Jesus Lover of My Soul

Key of F (Martin)

Jesus, lover of my soul,
Let me to Thy bosom fly,
While the nearer waters roll,
While the tempest still is high:
Hide me, O my Savior, hide,
Till the storm of life is past;
Safe into the haven guide,
O receive my soul at last.

Other refuge have I none;
Hangs my helpless soul on Thee;
Leave, oh, leave me not alone,
Still support and comfort me.
All my trust on Thee is stayed,
All my help from Thee I bring;
Cover my defenseless head
With the shadow of Thy wing.

Thou, O Christ, art all I want;
More than all in Thee I find;
Raise the fallen, cheer the faint,
Heal the sick, and lead the blind.
Just and holy is Thy name,
I am all unrighteousness;
False, and full of sin, I am,
Thou art full of truth and grace.

Plenteous grace with Thee is found,
Grace to pardon all my sin;
Let the healing streams abound;
Make and keep me pure within.
Thou of life the fountain art,
Freely let me take of Thee;
Spring Thou up within my heart,
Rise to all eternity.

Faith of Our Fathers   *H. 458*   150

Key of A flat.

Faith of our fathers! living still
In spite of dungeon, fire, and sword;
O how our hearts beat high with joy
When-e'er we hear that glorious word!
Faith of our fathers! holy faith!
We will be true to thee till death!

Our fathers, chained in prisons dark,
Were still in heart and conscience free:
How sweet would be their children's
    fate,

If they, like them, could die for thee!
Faith of our fathers! holy faith!
We will be true to thee till death!

Faith of our fathers! we will love
Both friend and foe in all our strife;
And preach thee, too, as love knows
    how,
By kindly words and virtuous life:
Faith of our fathers! holy faith!
We will be true to thee till death!

Loving Kindness   151

Key of A flat.

Awake, my soul, to joyful lays,
    And sing thy great Redeemer's
    praise;
He justly claims a song from me,
    His loving kindness, oh, how free!

He saw me ruined in the fall,
    Yet loved me, notwithstanding all;
He saved me from my lost estate,
    His loving kindness, oh, how
    great!

Tho' numerous hosts of mighty foes,
    Tho' earth and hell my way op-
    pose,
He safely leads my soul along,
    His loving kindness, oh, how
    strong!

When trouble, like a gloomy cloud,
    Has gathered thick, and thunder-
    ed loud,
He near my soul has always stood,
    His loving kindness, oh, how
    good!

All Hail the Power of Jesus' Name   *H. 466*   152

Key of G.

All hail the pow'r of Jesus' name!
    Let angels prostrate fall;
|| :Bring forth the royal diadem,
    And crown Him Lord of all :||

Ye chosen seed of Israel's race,
    A remnant weak and small,
|| :Hail Him who saves you by His
    grace,
And crown Him Lord of all :||

Ye Gentile sinners, ne'er forget
    The worm-wood and the gall
|| :Go, spread your trophies at His feet,
    And crown Him Lord of all :||

Let ev'ry kindred, ev'ry tribe
    On this terrestrial ball,
|| :To Him all majesty ascribe,
    And crown Him Lord of all :||

O that, with yonder sacred throng,
    We at His feet may fall,
|| :We'll join the everlasting song,
    And crown Him Lord of all :||

153 *H.361* Nearer My God to Thee

Key of G

Nearer, my God, to Thee,
  Nearer to Thee;
E'en though it be a cross
  That raiseth me;
Still all my song shall be,
|| :Nearer, my God, to Thee :||
  Nearer to Thee.

Tho' like a wanderer,
  Daylight all gone,
Darkness be over me,
  My rest a stone,
Yet in my dreams I'd be,
|| :Nearer, my God, to Thee :||
  Nearer to Thee,

There let the way appear,
  Steps up to heav'n;
All that Thou sendest me
  In mercy giv'n;
Angels to beckon me,
|| :Nearer, my God, to Thee :||
  Nearer to Thee.

Then with my waking tho'ts
  Bright with Thy praise,
Out of my stony griefs
  Bethel I'll raise;
So by my woes to be,
|| :Nearer, my God, to Thee :||
  Nearer to Thee.

154 *H.398* Blessed Assurance

Key of D.

Blessed assurance, Jesus is mine!
Oh, what a foretaste of glory divine!
Heir of salvation, purchase of God,
Born of His Spirit, washed in His
  blood.

Refrain:
|| :This is my story, this is my song,
  Praising my Savior all the day long :||

Perfect submission, perfect delight,
Visions of rapture now burst on my
  sight;
Angels descending bring from above
Echoes of mercy, whispers of love.

Perfect submission, all is at rest,
I in my Savior am happy and blest;
Watching and waiting, looking above,
Filled with His goodness, lost in
  His love.

155 *H.226* What a Friend We Have in Jesus

Key of F.

What a friend we have in Jesus,
  All our sins and griefs to bear;
What a privilege to carry
  Ev'rything to God in prayer!
O what peace we often forfeit,
  O what needless pain we bear,
All because we do not carry
  Ev'rything to God in prayer.

Have we trials and temptations?
  Is there trouble anywhere?
We should never be discouraged:
  Take it to the Lord in prayer!

Can we find a friend so faithful,
  Who will all our sorrows share?
Jesus knows our ev'ry weakness;
  Take it to the Lord in prayer!

Are we weak and heavy laden,
  Cumbered with a load of care?
Precious Savior, still our refuge;
  Take it to the Lord in prayer!
Do thy friends despise, forsake thee?
  Take it to the Lord in prayer!
In His arms He'll take and shield
  thee,
  Thou wilt find a solace there.

SELECT SCRIPTURES

1.

PRAYER
John 14:13

And whatsoever ye shall ask in my name that will I do that the Father may be glorified in the Son.

Matt. 6:9-13

9 After this manner therefore pray ye: Our Father which art in heaven, Hallowed be thy name.

10 Thy kingdom come. Thy will be done in earth, as it is in heaven.

11 Give us this day our daily bread.

12 And forgive us our debts, as we forgive our debtors.

13 And lead us not into temptation, but deliver us from evil: For thine is the kingdom, and the power, and the glory, for ever. Amen.

2.

GOD'S WORD
Psa. 119:1-11

1 Blessed are the undefiled in the way, who walk in the law of the Lord.

2 Blessed are they that keep his testimonies, and that seek him with the whole heart.

3 They also do no iniquity: they walk in his ways.

4 Thou hast commanded us to keep thy precepts diligently.

5 O that my ways were directed to keep thy statutes!

6 Then shall I not be ashamed, when I have respect unto all thy commandments.

7 I will praise thee with uprightness of heart, when I shall have learned thy righteous judgments.

8 I will keep thy statutes: O forsake me not utterly.

9 Wherewithal shall a young man cleanse his way? by taking heed thereto according to thy word.

10 With my whole heart have I sought thee: O let me not wander from thy commandments.

11 Thy word have I hid in mine heart, that I might not sin against thee.

3.

THE WORD OF GOD IN THE HOME
Deut. 6:4-92

4 Hear, O Israel: the Lord our God is one Lord:

5 And thou shalt love the Lord thy God with all thine heart, and with all thy soul, and with all thy might.

6 And these words, which I command thee this day, shall be in thine heart:

7 And thou shalt teach them diligently unto thy children, and shalt talk of them when thou sittest in thine house, and when thou walkest by the way, and when thou liest down, and when thou risest up.

8 And thou shalt bind them for a sign upon thine hand, and they shall be as frontlets between thine eyes.

9 And thou shalt write them upon the posts of thine house, and on thy gates.

4.

TRIUMPHANT PRAISE
Psa. 100:1-5

1 Make a joyful noise unto the Lord, all ye lands.

2 Serve the Lord with gladness: come before his presence with singing.

3 Know ye that the Lord he is God: it is he that hath made us, and not we ourselves; we are his people, and the sheep of his pasture.

4 Enter into his gates with thanksgiving, and into his courts with praise: be thankful unto him, and bless his name.

5 For the Lord is good; his mercy is everlasting; and his truth endureth to all generations.

5.

GOD IS GLORIFIED
Psa. 19:1-14

1 The heavens declare the glory of God; and the firmament sheweth his handywork.

2 Day unto day uttereth speech, and night unto night sheweth knowledge.

3 There is no speech nor language, where their voice is not heard.

4 Their line is gone out through all the earth, and their words to the end of the world. In them hath he set a tabernacle for the sun,

5 Which is as a bridegroom coming out of his chamber, and rejoiceth as a strong man to run a race.

6 His going forth is from the end of the heaven, and his circuit unto the ends of it: and there is nothing hid from the heat thereof.

7 The law of the Lord is perfect, converting the soul; the testimony of the Lord is sure, making wise the simple.

8 The statutes of the Lord are right, rejoicing the heart: the commandment of the Lord is pure, enlightening the eyes.

9 The fear of the Lord is clean, enduring forever: the judgments of the Lord are true and righteous altogether.

10 More to be desired are they than gold, yea, than much fine gold: sweeter also than honey and the honeycomb.

11 Moreover by them is thy servant warned: and in keeping of them there is great reward.

12 Who can understand his errors? cleanse thou me from secret faults.

13 Keep back thy servant also from presumptuous sins; let them not have dominion over me: then shall I be upright, and I shall be innocent from the great transgression.

14 Let the words of my mouth and the meditation of my heart be acceptable in thy sight, O Lord, my strength, and my redeemer.

6.

THE SHEPHERD PSALM
Psa. 23:1-6

1 The Lord is my shepherd; I shall not want.

2 He maketh me to lie down in green pastures: he leadeth me beside the still waters.

3 He restoreth my soul: he leadeth me in the paths of righteousness for his name's sake.

4 Yea, though I walk through the valley of the shadow of death, I will fear no evil: for thou art with me; thy rod and thy staff they comfort me.

5 Thou preparest a table before me in the presence of mine enemies: thou anointest my head with oil; my cup runneth over.

6 Surely goodness and mercy shall follow me all the days of my life: and I will dwell in the house of the Lord for ever.

7.

PENITENCE
Psa. 51:1-4, 10-13

1 Have mercy upon me, O God, according to thy lovingkindness: according unto the multitude of thy tender mercies blot out my transgressions.

2 Wash me thoroughly from mine iniquity, and cleanse me from my sin.

3 For I acknowledge my transgressions: and my sin is ever before me.

4 Against thee, thee only, have I sinned, and done this evil in thy sight: that thou mightest be justified when thou speakest, and be clear when thou judgest.

10 Create in me a clean heart, O God; and renew a right spirit within me.

11 Cast me not away from thy presence; and take not thy holy spirit from me.

12 Restore unto me the joy of thy salvation; and uphold me with thy free spirit.

13 Then will I teach transgressors thy ways; and sinners shall be converted unto thee.

8.

THE RIGHTEOUS AND THE SINNER

Psa. 1:1-6

1 Blessed is the man that walketh not in the counsel of the ungodly, nor standeth in the way of sinners, nor sitteth in the seat of the scornful.

2 But his delight is in the law of the Lord; and in his law doth he meditate day and night.

3 And he shall be like a tree planted by the rivers of water, that bringeth forth his fruit in his season; his leaf also shall not wither; and whatsoever he doeth shall prosper.

4 The ungodly are not so: but are like the chaff which the wind driveth away.

5 Therefore the ungodly shall not stand in the judgment, nor sinners in the congregation of the righteous.

6 For the Lord knoweth the way of the righteous: but the way of the ungodly shall perish.

9.

THE MERCY OF THE LORD

Psa. 103:1-13

1 Bless the Lord, O my soul: and all that is within me, bless his holy name.

2 Bless the Lord, O my soul, and forget not all his benefits:

3 Who forgiveth all thine iniquities; who healeth all thy diseases;

4 Who redeemeth thy life from destruction; who crowneth thee with lovingkindness and tender mercies;

5 Who satisfieth thy mouth with good things; so that thy youth is renewed like the eagle's.

6 The Lord executeth righteousness and judgment for all that are oppressed.

7 He made known his ways unto Moses, his acts unto the children of Israel.

8 The Lord is merciful and gracious, slow to anger, and plenteous in mercy.

9 He will not always chide: neither will he keep his anger forever.

10 He hath not dealt with us after our sins; nor rewarded us according to our iniquities.

11 For as the heaven is high above the earth, so great is his mercy toward them that fear him.

12 As far as the east is from the west, so far hath he removed our transgressions from us.

13 Like as a father pitieth his children, so the Lord pitieth them that fear him.

10.

THE BEATITUDES

Matt. 5:3-11

3 Blessed are the poor in spirit: for their's is the kingdom of heaven.

4 Blessed are they that mourn: for they shall be comforted.

5 Blessed are the meek: for they shall inherit the earth.

6 Blessed are they which do hunger and thirst after righteousness: for they shall be filled.

7 Blessed are the merciful: for they shall obtain mercy.

8 Blessed are the pure in heart: for they shall see God.

9 Blessed are the peacemakers: for they shall be called the children of God.

10 Blessed are they which are persecuted for righteousness' sake: for their's is the kingdom of heaven.

11 Blessed are ye, when men shall revile you, and persecute you, and shall say all manner of evil against you falsely, for my sake.

11.

THE LORD IS THY KEEPER

Psa. 121:1-8

1 I will lift up mine eyes unto the hills, from whence cometh my help.

2 My help cometh from the Lord, which made heaven and earth.

3 He will not suffer thy foot to be moved: he that keepeth thee will not slumber.

4 Behold, he that keepeth Israel shall neither slumber nor sleep.

5 The Lord is thy keeper: the Lord is thy shade upon thy right hand.

6 The sun shall not smite thee by day, nor the moon by night.

7 The Lord shall preserve thee from all evil: he shall preserve thy soul.

8 The Lord shall preserve thy going out and thy coming in from this time forth, and even for evermore.

12.

CONSTANT COMPANIONSHIP

Psa. 139:1-12

1 O Lord, thou hast searched me, and known me.

2 Thou knowest my downsitting and mine uprising, thou understandest my thought afar off.

3 Thou compassest my path and my lying down, and art acquainted with all my ways.

4 For there is not a word in my tongue, but, lo, O Lord, thou knowest it altogether.

5 Thou hast beset me behind and before, and laid thine hand upon me.

6 Such knowledge is too wonderful for me; it is high, I cannot attain unto it.

7 Whither shall I go from thy spirit? or whither shall I flee from thy presence?

8 If I ascend up into heaven, thou art there: if I make my bed in hell, behold, thou art there.

9 If I take the wings of the morning, and dwell in the uttermost parts of the sea;

10 Even there shall thy hand lead me, and thy right hand shall hold me.

11 If I say, Surely the darkness shall cover me; even the night shall be light about me.

12 Yea, the darkness hideth not from thee; but the night shineth as the day: the darkness and the light are both alike to thee.

13.

DELIGHT IN THE HOUSE OF THE LORD

Psa. 84:1-12

1 How amiable are thy tabernacles, O Lord of hosts!

2 My soul longeth, yea, even fainteth for the courts of the Lord: my heart and my flesh crieth out for the living God.

3 Yea, the sparrow hath found an house, and the swallow a nest for herself, where she may lay her young, even thine altars, O Lord of hosts, my King, and my God.

4 Blessed are they that dwell in thy house: they will be still praising thee. Selah.

5 Blessed is the man whose strength is in thee; in whose heart are the ways of them.

6 Who passing through the valley of Baca make it a well; the rain also filleth the pools.

7 They go from strength to strength, every one of them in Zion appeareth before God.

8 O Lord God of hosts, hear my prayer: give ear, O God of Jacob. Selah.

9 Behold, O God our shield, and look upon the face of thine anointed.

10 For a day in thy courts is better than a thousand. I had rather be a doorkeeper in the house of my God, than to dwell in the tents of wickedness.

11 For the Lord God is a sun and

shield: the Lord will give grace and glory: no good thing will he withhold from them that walk uprightly.

12 O Lord of hosts, blessed is the man that trusteth in thee.

14.

THE CHRISTMAS STORY
Luke 2:7-20

7 And she brought forth her first-born son, and wrapped him in swaddling clothes, and laid him in a manger; because there was no room for them in the inn.

8 And there were in the same country shepherds abiding in the field, keeping watch over their flocks by night.

9 And, lo, the angel of the Lord came upon them, and the glory of the Lord shone round about them: and they were sore afraid.

10 And the angel said unto them, Fear not: for, behold, I bring you good tidings of great joy, which shall be to all people.

11 For unto you is born this day in the city of David a Saviour, which is Christ the Lord.

12 And this shall be a sign unto you; Ye shall find the babe wrapped in swaddling clothes, lying in a manger.

13 And suddenly there was with the angel a multitude of the heavenly host praising God, and saying,

14 Glory to God in the highest, and on earth peace, good will toward men.

15 And it came to pass, as the angels were gone away from them into heaven, the shepherds said one to another, Let us now go even unto Bethlehem, and see this thing which is come to pass, which the Lord hath made known unto us.

16 And they came with haste, and found Mary, and Joseph, and the babe lying in a manger.

17 And when they had seen it, they made known abroad the saying which was told them concerning this child.

18 And all they that heard it wondered at those things which were told them by the shepherds.

19 But Mary kept all these things, and pondered them in her heart.

20 And the shepherds returned, glorifying and praising God for all the things that they had heard and seen, as it was told unto them.

15.

THE EASTER STORY
Matt. 28:1-10

1 In the end of the sabbath, as it began to dawn toward the first day of the week, came Mary Magdalene and the other Mary to see the sepulchre.

2 And, behold, there was a great earthquake: for the angel of the Lord descended from heaven, and came and rolled back the stone from the door, and sat upon it.

3 His countenance was like lightning, and his raiment white as snow:

4 And for fear of him the keepers did shake, and became as dead men.

5 And the angel answered and said unto the women, Fear not ye: for I know that ye seek Jesus, which was crucified.

6 He is not here: for he is risen, as he said. Come, see the place where the Lord lay.

7 And go quickly, and tell his disciples that he is risen from the dead; and, behold, he goeth before you into Galilee; there shall ye see him: lo, I have told you.

8 And they departed quickly from the sepulchre with fear and great joy; and did run to bring his disciples word.

9 And as they went to tell his disciples, behold Jesus met them, saying, All hail. And they came and held him by the feet, and worshipped him.

10 Then said Jesus unto them, Be not afraid: go tell my brethren that they go into Galilee, and there shall they see me.

16.

THE TEN COMMANDMENTS

Ex. 20:2-17

I am the Lord thy God, which have brought thee out of the land of Egypt, out of the house of bondage.

I. Thou shalt have no other gods before me.

II. Thou shalt not make unto thee any graven image, or any likeness of any thing that is in heaven above, or that is in the earth beneath, or that is in the water under the earth; Thou shalt not bow down thyself to them, nor serve them: for I the Lord thy God am a jealous God, visiting the iniquity of the fathers upon the children unto the third and fourth generation of them that hate me; and shewing mercy unto thousands of them that love me, and keep my commandments.

III. Thou shalt not take the name of the Lord thy God in vain; for the Lord will not hold him guiltless that taketh his name in vain.

IV. Remember the sabbath day, to keep it holy. Six days shalt thou labor, and do all thy work: But the seventh day is the sabbath of the Lord thy God: in it thou shalt not do any work, thou, nor thy son, nor thy daughter, thy manservant, nor thy maidservant, nor thy cattle, nor thy stranger that is within thy gates: For in six days the Lord made heaven and earth, the sea, and all that in them is, and rested the seventh day: wherefore the Lord blessed the sabbath day, and hallowed it.

V. Honor thy father and thy mother: that thy days may be long upon the land which the Lord thy God giveth thee.

VI. Thou shalt not kill.

VII. Thou shalt not commit adultery.

VIII. Thou shalt not steal.

IX. Thou shalt not bear false witness against thy neighbor.

X. Thou shalt not covet thy neighbour's house, thou shalt not covet thy neighbor's wife, nor his man-servant, nor his maidservant, nor his ox, nor his ass, nor any thing that is thy neighbour's.

17.

LOVE

I Cor. 13:1-13

1 Though I speak with the tongues of men and of angels, and have not charity, I am become as sounding brass, or a tinkling cymbal.

2 And though I have the gift of prophecy, and understand all mysteries, and all knowledge; and though I have all faith, so that I could remove mountains, and have not charity, I am nothing.

3 And though I bestow all my goods to feed the poor, and though I give my body to be burned, and have not charity, it profiteth me nothing.

4 Charity suffereth long, and is kind; charity envieth not; charity vaunteth not itself, is not puffed up,

5 Doth not behave itself unseemly, seeketh not her own, is not easily provoked, thinketh no evil;

6 Rejoiceth not in iniquity, but rejoiceth in the truth;

7 Beareth all things, believeth all things, hopeth all things, endureth all things.

8 Charity never faileth: but whether there be prophecies, they shall fail; whether there be tongues, they shall cease; whether there be knowledge, it shall vanish away.

9 For we know in part, and we prophesy in part.

10 But when that which is perfect is come, then that which is in part shall be done away.

11 When I was a child, I spake as a child, I understood as a child, I thought as a child: but when I became a man, I put away childish things.

12 For now we see through a glass,

darkly; but then face to face: now I know in part; but then shall I know even as also I am known.

13 And now abideth faith, hope, charity, these three; but the greatest of these is charity.

18.

REVERENCE FOR THE HOUSE OF THE LORD

Psa. 89:5-8

5 And the heavens shall praise thy wonders, O Lord: thy faithfulness also in the congregation of the saints.

6 For who in the heaven can be compared unto the Lord? who among the sons of the mighty can be likened unto the Lord?

7 God is greatly to be feared in the assembly of the saints, and to be had in reverence of all them that are about him.

8 O Lord God of hosts, who is a strong Lord like unto thee? or to thy faithfulness round about thee?

Eccl. 5:1

1 Keep thy foot when thou goest to the house of God, and be more ready to hear, than to give the sacrifice of fools: for they consider not that they do evil.

19.

THE SUFFERING SAVIOUR

Isa. 53:1-7

1 Who hath believed our report? and to whom is the arm of the Lord revealed?

2 For he shall grow up before him as a tender plant, and as a root out of a dry ground: he hath no form nor comeliness; and when we shall see him, there is no beauty that we should desire him.

3 He is despised and rejected of men; a man of sorrows, and acquainted with grief: and we hid as it were our faces from him; he was despised, and we esteemed him not.

4 Surely he hath borne our griefs, and carried our sorrows: yet we did esteem him stricken, smitten of God, and afflicted.

5 But he was wounded for our transgressions, he was bruised for our iniquities: the chastisement of our peace was upon him; and with his stripes we are healed.

6 All we like sheep have gone astray; we have turned every one to his own way; and the Lord hath laid on him the iniquity of us all.

7 He was oppressed, and he was afflicted, yet he opened not his mouth: he is brought as a lamb to the slaughter, and as a sheep before her shearers is dumb, so he openeth not his mouth.

20.

WE WILL SERVE THE LORD

Josh. 24:14-18

14 Now therefore fear the Lord, and serve him in sincerity and in truth: and put away the gods which your fathers served on the other side of the flood, and in Egypt; and serve ye the Lord.

15 And if it seem evil unto you to serve the Lord, choose you this day whom ye will serve; whether the gods which your fathers served that were on the other side of the flood, or the gods of the Amorites, in whose land ye dwell: but as for me and my house, we will serve the Lord.

16 And the people answered and said, God forbid that we should forsake the Lord, to serve other gods;

17 For the Lord our God, he it is that brought us up and our fathers out of the land of Egypt, from the house of bondage, and which did those great signs in our sight, and preserved us in all the way wherein we went, and among all the people through whom we passed:

18 And the Lord drave them out from before us all the people, even the Amorites which dwelt in the land: therefore will we also serve the Lord; for he is our God.

21.

SERVING THE LORD IN HEAVEN

Rev. 7:9-17

9 After this I beheld, and, lo, a great multitude, which no man could number, of all nations, and kindreds, and people, and tongues, stood before the throne, and before the Lamb, clothed with white robes, and palms in their hands;

10 And cried with a loud voice, saying, Salvation to our God which sitteth upon the throne, and unto the Lamb.

11 And all the angels stood round about the throne, and about the elders and the four beasts, and fell before the throne on their faces, and worshipped God,

12 Saying, Amen: Blessing, and glory, and wisdom, and thanksgiving, and honour, and power, and might, be unto our God for ever and ever. Amen.

13 And one of the elders answered, saying unto me, What are these which are arrayed in white robes? and whence came they?

14 And I said unto him, Sir, thou knowest. And he said to me, These are they which came out of great tribulation, and have washed their robes, and made them white in the blood of the Lamb.

15 Therefore are they before the throne of God, and serve him day and night in his temple: and he that sitteth on the throne shall dwell among them.

16 They shall hunger no more, neither thirst any more; neither shall the sun light on them, nor any heat.

17 For the Lamb which is in the midst of the throne shall feed them, and shall lead them unto living fountains of waters: and God shall wipe away all tears from their eyes.

INDEX

Titles in caps; first lines in small type.

INDEX